Written by

Michelle Powers, Teri Barenborg,
Tari Sexton, and Lauren Monroe

Editors: Christie Weltz and Jasmine Tabrizi
Designer/Production: Kammy Peyton
Art Director: Moonhee Pak
Project Director: Stacey Faulkner

DEDICATION

This book is dedicated to all of the educators and children who have inspired us to make education a hands-on experience and, most importantly, instilled within us a lifelong love of learning.

ACKNOWLEDGMENTS

First and foremost, we would like to thank our families and friends who have supported us in so many ways—from the steadfast support of our chosen career path and passion all the way through the inspiration and creation of this series of books. Each of us has an amazing support system that has not only encouraged us but also made it possible for us to devote our time to this project. A sincere thank-you to our colleagues, both past and present, as well as all the educators who have inspired us to create a collection of lessons that encourage students to grow and take ownership of their learning. Without the continued support and encouragement of our dear friend Lynn Howard, these books would not have been possible.

Our school district, St. Lucie Public Schools, known for being the first Kids at Hope school district in the state of Florida, motivated us to build a culture of learning where students state daily that "All children are capable of success. No exceptions." This mindset, along with the work of Carol Dweck and her focus on self-efficacy through a growth mindset, has inspired us to develop lessons that encourage problem solving and perseverance, allowing students to learn from their mistakes.

We would like to thank the various teachers who have opened their doors to us and, more importantly, the students in those classrooms who have tested these exciting lessons during their development. These teachers have allowed us to model, motivate, and encourage them to transition from the "Sage on the Stage" to a "Guide on the Side," giving students the opportunity to drive their own learning.

FOREWORD

Science instruction has changed. Many of us can remember the traditional lecture and note giving model of instruction that had been used for years. I was very alone in my middle school earth science classroom and had no support, no textbook or curriculum guide. Living day to day with content that was totally unfamiliar to me, I taught the same way to all students and didn't realize that many of them were not engaged or learning. I had to change and allow for more engagement, exploration, and experimentation. It quickly became the way I taught, and students benefited from the problem solving, collaboration, and inquiry-based activities. When I began my science teaching career years ago, I would have appreciated a resource that provided me with a set of classroom lessons that would challenge and motivate my students.

The Next Generation Science Standards are placing a great emphasis on how we "do science" in the classroom. The integration of science, technology, engineering, arts, and math (STEAM) provides multiple opportunities to include problem solving, engineering practices, and literacy while engaging and motivating students in real-world science experiences.

I really like this book. These lessons are perfect for any teacher who may or may not feel comfortable with teaching science. I really like that the lessons are aligned with the 5E Instructional Model (engage, explore, explain, elaborate, and evaluate). Teachers who use the lessons will address the 5E model and challenge their students with the engineering process. The authors are a team of educators who understand how to teach science. Their teaching has evolved from a traditional approach to becoming facilitators of science knowledge. Teri, Lauren, Michelle, and Tari have spent time learning about the changes in science education and how to design effective science classroom environments. As a professional development associate, I spent three years with them as they explored how to create a balanced science program focused on the Next Generation Science Standards. They invested a large amount of time researching what works and implementing those best practices in their classrooms. I have had the opportunity to be in all of their classrooms and see the engagement and excitement as students collaborate on real-world engineering design problems. The teachers continually reinforce the idea that their students ARE scientists and must practice the habits of scientists. A by-product of these teachers' efforts is a book that other teachers can use today in their classrooms to make it exciting to teach and learn about science!

I am honored that Teri, Lauren, Michelle, and Tari asked me to write the foreword for their book. These teachers truly live and breathe quality science teaching and learning. Their passion, dedication, and commitment to effective science instruction make the activities and ideas in this book invaluable to anyone who wants to get excited about STEAM in their classroom.

Lynn F. Howard
Author and Professional Development Associate
Five Easy Steps to a Balanced Science Program

TABLE OF CONTENTS

INTRODUCTION

Science, technology, engineering, art, and math work together to make learning fun!

The Next Generation Science Standards place a greater emphasis on science, technology, engineering, arts, and math (STEAM) in today's classrooms. Schools are implementing and encouraging strong STEAM programs in classrooms in order to provide critical thinking lessons that meet the content standards. STEAM lessons should include problem-solving skills, enhance learning across various disciplines, promote student inquiry, and engage students with real-world situations. Students should be exposed to careers in the STEAM fields and develop skills such as communication, data analysis, following a process, designing a product, and argumentation based on evidence, all while cementing effective collaboration techniques that are necessary for a successful career in STEAM fields.

The lessons in this book are intended to support teachers in implementing the engineering design process in their classroom while integrating national standards from other disciplines. In the engineering design process, teachers become a facilitator rather than the instructional focus. Teachers encourage and guide students to work as a team to find a creative solution without providing step-by-step instructions. The engineering design process shifts away from the long-standing process of the scientific method by placing more emphasis on inquiry. Students are inspired to act as scientists and engineers through the use of sketches, diagrams, mathematical relationships, and literacy connections. By creating their very own models and products based on background information from their studies, students are immediately engaged through a meaningful, rewarding lesson.

Each lesson begins by presenting students with a design challenge scenario, or hook, in order to immediately excite students with a real-world situation that they are on a mission to solve. Students are then given a dilemma, mission, and blueprint design sheet and are asked to collaborate with team members to create several prototypes. Teams are required to choose one prototype to present to their teacher before gathering materials and constructing the chosen design. After testing out their design, teams take part in a class discussion and modify their ideas for redesign and improvement of their prototype. Finally, teams are asked to create a justification piece in order to sell their new prototype. Suggestions for justification projects are provided for each design challenge and include writing a persuasive letter, creating an advertisement or presentation, recording a video, or any other creative ideas they come up with in response to the challenge.

The engaging STEAM design challenge lessons in this book

- Promote analytical and reflective thinking

- Enhance learning across various disciplines

- Encourage students to collaborate to solve real-world design challenges

- Integrate national standards

- Are classroom tested

HOW TO USE THIS BOOK

STEAM design challenges follow the engineering practices that have become recently known in the education field. Engineering practices teach students to solve a problem by designing, creating, and justifying their design. With this model in mind, teachers shift from a "giver of information" to a "facilitator of knowledge." Instead of leading children to the right conclusion through experimental steps, the teacher allows them to work through the process themselves, often changing their plan to improve their original design.

STEAM design challenges allow art to support and enhance the learning of science and math while the engineering process is followed. Students will often use, or be encouraged to use, technology to facilitate their learning. The teacher's role as facilitator allows him or her to guide student thinking by asking questions instead of giving answers. Each lesson covers cross-curricular standards and supports teacher planning for collaboration with other teachers.

Typically, science is not taught as often in elementary school as English, reading, writing, and math, so assignments have been included within the lessons that will assist in giving students skills and practice in those other key subjects.

Lessons focus on key national science standards that are required for many standardized tests and include core English language arts and math standards. National engineering standards as well as national arts and national technology standards are also included in the lessons.

The 5E Instructional Model emphasizes building new ideas using existing knowledge. The components of this model—*Engage, Explore, Explain, Elaborate,* and *Evaluate*—are also a key design feature in the structure of each design challenge. Each design challenge requires the students to respond using mathematical, written, oral, and theatrical skills that are developmentally appropriate while working through each phase of the 5E model.

PHASES OF THE 5E MODEL

ENGAGE

Students make connections between past and present learning and focus their thinking on learning outcomes in the activity.

EXPLORE

Students continue to build on their knowledge of their learning through exploration and manipulation of materials.

EXPLAIN

Students support their understanding of the concepts through verbal or written communication. This is also a time when students may demonstrate new skills and when teachers can introduce new vocabulary.

ELABORATE

Students extend their understanding of concepts by obtaining more information about a topic through new experiences.

EVALUATE

Students assess their understanding of key concepts and skills.

LESSON PLAN FORMAT

Each lesson centers around the Design Challenge Purpose and has two distinct sections—Setting the Stage and STEAM in Action.

- Setting the Stage provides an overview of the lesson, suggested time frame, the background knowledge needed for the teacher and students as well as the standards, target vocabulary, and materials needed.

- STEAM in Action outlines the step-by-step procedure for implementing the lesson.

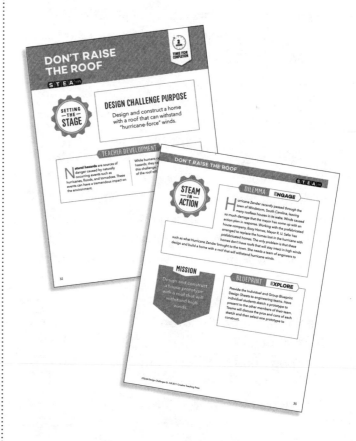

LESSON PLAN COMPONENTS

SETTING THE STAGE

Header: This section includes the title, suggested time frame for completing the lesson, and the STEAM acronym, in which the capital letters denote the main disciplines that are highlighted in each particular lesson.

Time: A suggested approximate total time for completing each lesson is provided. Because the amount of time teachers have to teach science varies within different states, districts, schools, and even grade levels, you may need to break up the lesson into smaller segments over the course of several days. Natural breaks occur between design and construction, between construction and testing, and between testing and justification.

You may choose to use the lesson ideas in the Student Development section to deepen prior knowledge or you may have your students use the literacy connections and any reputable websites you are familiar with. The lesson ideas in the Justification section are included as an optional extension of the core lesson. None of the activities before or after the core lesson are included in the time estimates. Refer to the suggested lesson timeline on page 11.

Design Challenge Purpose: This is the statement that sets the stage for the design challenge and outlines student objectives and expectations for what they should learn by completing the design challenge.

Teacher Development: This section provides background information about the science content being addressed in the lesson. Information included assists the teacher in understanding key science concepts. We understand that professional development at the elementary teacher level is often geared toward instructional delivery instead of content, especially in the content area of science. This section is provided to help support teachers who may not be as familiar with science content.

Student Development: This section contains a description of the concepts students will need to understand to complete the design challenge successfully. A link to the STEAM Dreamers website, which has active web links and additional suggested lesson ideas for deepening students' understanding of relevant science concepts, can be found on the inside front cover of this book.

Standards: This section lists specific standards for science, technology, engineering, art, math, and English language arts, along with the science and engineering practices and crosscutting concepts. These standards may apply to the activities in the challenges or in the justifications that follow. Please make sure that you review the standards for each of the lessons. The website for each set of standards is listed on page 13.

Target Vocabulary: This section lists target vocabulary to support and enhance the lesson content and to deepen students' understanding of the terms. These vocabulary terms are related to the academic content that the design challenge focuses on; can be used throughout the design challenge when in group discussion; and are an integral component of the standards covered in the challenge. Reviewing the target vocabulary prior to beginning the design challenge is recommended as students need to apply their knowledge of the science concepts and target vocabulary when solving the challenges. Ultimately, the target vocabulary should be revisited multiple times throughout the lesson.

Materials: This section lists materials and equipment that have been selected for the lessons. All materials are meant to be easy to find, inexpensive to purchase, recycled, or commonly available for free. Substitute with similar items if you have them on hand, or visit www.SteamDreamers.com for substitute suggestions.

Literacy Connections: This section lists books or articles that are meant to be used with students prior to the design challenge in order to strengthen their background knowledge and to enhance the integration of literacy in STEAM. These connections can be used during the daily classroom reading block, during small and/or whole-group instruction.

Current literacy connections for each lesson can be accessed through our website: www.SteamDreamers.com.

STEAM IN ACTION

The Dilemma: This section includes a unique real-world dilemma or scenario that hooks the students and gets them excited to solve the problem. The dilemma may include a plausible circumstance or a wild story designed to make them think. When planning the design of their prototype, student should ask themselves questions such as *Who is the client? What do we need to create? What is the purpose of the creation? What is the ultimate goal?* Students should discuss these questions with other members of their team and record their responses in their science notebooks.

Note: This is the Engage portion of the lesson, as outlined in the 5E Instructional Model.

The Mission: This section includes the defined challenge statement. This is ultimately the goal that the students are trying to reach.

Blueprint Design: This section instructs students on how to focus their thinking in order to solve the problem. Individual team members design their own plans for prototypes and list the pros and cons of their designs. Each team member reviews the Blueprint Design Sheet of every other team member and records the pros and cons he or she sees. The team then chooses which member's design it will move forward with. This is where students have the opportunity to discuss and make decisions based on their analysis on the Individual Blueprint Design Sheets. Students are allowed and encouraged to add their artistic touches to their thinking. Individual and Group Blueprint Design Sheets are found in the Appendix.

Note: This is the Explore portion of the lesson, as outlined in the 5E Instructional Model.

Engineering Design Process: In this section of the lesson, teams will take their group's selected prototype through the engineering design process to create, test, analyze, and redesign as necessary until they have successfully completed their mission.

- The first step in the process is the Engineering Task in which teams will engineer their prototype.

- Students will then test their prototype based upon the mission statement.

- The analysis of their testing will include data collection and determination of success.

- The Redesign and Retest cycle will continue until the team has successfully completed the mission.

Helpful Tips: In this section you'll find suggestions designed to address common issues that may arise during the design challenges. Some tips are geared toward the steps in the engineering design process, and some are more lesson-specific.

Reflections: This section provides suggestions for reflective questions to ask students to help guide and facilitate their thinking at various stages within the engineering design process. It is recommended that students record these questions and their reflections in a science notebook. See pages 16–19 for more information on using a science notebook.

Note: This is the Explain and Elaborate portion of the lesson, as outlined in the 5E Instructional Model.

Justification: This is the stage of the lesson where students apply what they learned in a meaningful and creative way through different mediums, such as technology and the arts. These justifications can occur in many forms: a formal letter, an advertisement, a poem, a jingle, a skit, or a technology-enhanced presentation.

Note: This is the Evaluate portion of the lesson, as outlined in the 5E Instructional Model.

SUGGESTED LESSON TIMELINE

Lesson Progression:

1. Teacher Development/Student Development/Literacy Connections

2. Dilemma/Mission/Blueprint Design

3. Engineering Task/Test Trial/Analyze/Redesign/Reflection

4. Justification

If the lesson will be spread out over multiple days:

Day 1: Teacher Development/Student Development/Literacy Connections

Day 2: Dilemma/Mission/Blueprint Design

Day 3: Engineering Task/Test Trial

Days 4-6: Analyze/Redesign/Reflection (Can be spread over 3 days)

Days 7-8: Justification

THE APPENDIX

Lesson-Specific Activity Pages: Some lessons include specific activity pages for enhancing or completing the design challenges. They are found in the Appendix section.

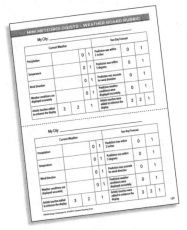

Blueprint Design Sheets: Every lesson requires students to first use the Individual Blueprint Design Sheet to create and list the pros and cons of their and their teammates' designs. Students will discuss their designs with team members and choose one design to use for building their prototype. This design, and reasons why it was chosen, are recorded on the Group Blueprint Design Sheet.

Budget Planning Chart: Any of the lessons can implement a budget for an added mathematical challenge. Prior to the start of the challenge, assign each material a cost and display for the class to reference throughout the challenge. Then decide on an overall budget for the materials. Some lessons may already provide a suggested budget. Students can use the Budget Planning Chart to itemize materials and identify the total cost of the materials needed to complete the challenge. The chart is blank to allow for more flexibility with the materials needed for specific challenges. Ensure students have a limit to what they can spend during the challenge. You can chose not to incorporate a budget if you are short on time. The time needed to assign specific material costs is not included in the overall completion time for the lessons.

Rubric: A rubric for grading the STEAM challenges is included. This rubric focuses on the engineering process. However, it does not include a means to assess the justification components.

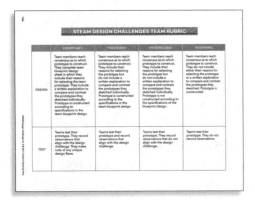

STEAM Job Cards: If your students are struggling with the collaboration process, try assigning them specific roles. Suggestions for jobs are provided on the STEAM Job Cards. Four students per team is recommended. The Accounts Manager role will only occur during the design challenges that involve a budget. In these cases, one student will have two roles, one of which is the Accounts Manager.

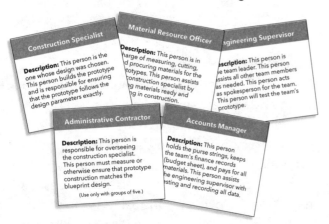

STEAM Money: The use of STEAM money is a fun way to engage students and connect the design challenges that incorporate budgets to the real world by having teams "purchase" materials. The use of STEAM money is completely optional. The following suggestions are offered should you choose to incorporate STEAM money into any of your lessons.

- Print multiple copies and laminate for durability and multiple use.

- Enlist the help of a parent volunteer to prepare the STEAM money at the beginning of the year.

- Assign material costs with the class before beginning lessons with budgets, or incorporate this into your long-range planning before school begins. This only has to be done one time. The budget is not set in stone. You may adjust the total budget amount and/or the materials cost according to students' math ability.

Glossary: A glossary of content-related terms has been provided for use as a teacher reference. Or make copies and distribute to students to include in their science notebooks.

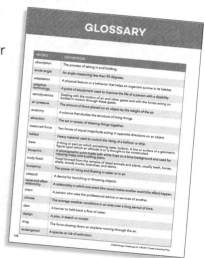

THE STANDARDS

SCIENCE

www.nextgenscience.org/search-standards-dci

The Next Generation Science Standards are arranged by disciplinary core ideas (DCI). When accessing these standards, search by standard and DCI. The standards are identified in the lessons by grade level and DCI. (e.g., 5-ESS3-1–Grade 5, Earth and Human Activity, Standard 1).

TECHNOLOGY

www.iste.org/standards

The International Society for Technology in Education (ISTE) publishes the national technology standards. Each of the standards is categorized into four main categories.

1. Creativity and innovation
2. Communication and collaboration
3. Research and information fluency
4. Critical thinking, problem solving, and decision making

Within each of these categories there are more specific indicators that are identified by a letter. Standards within the lessons will be indicated by the category (e.g., ISTE.1).

ENGINEERING

www.nextgenscence.org/search-standards-dci

The Next Generation Science Standards identify the engineering standards as well. They are categorized by the grade band of 3-5 (e.g., 3-5-ETS1-1).

ARTS

www.nationalartsstandards.org
www.corestandards.org/ELA-Literacy

The National Core Arts Standards are divided into four categories:

1. Creating
2. Performing/Presenting/Producing
3. Responding
4. Connecting

Each of these categories contains anchor standards. Within the lesson, the standards will be identified by the category and the anchor standard (e.g., Creating, Anchor Standard #1).

In addition to performance standards, the literacy standards are embedded throughout the lessons. Each lesson identifies specific English language arts (ELA) standards (e.g., CCSS.ELA-LITERACY.W.5.2).

MATH

www.corestandards.org/math

The Common Core Math Standards are divided into two categories:

1. Content
2. Practice

The content standards are those items such as computation and geometry. The practice standards are a framework for ensuring that students are practicing math in a meaningful and appropriate manner.

The content standards will be identified first in the Math Standards column and the Math Practice Standards will be underneath (e.g., CCSS.MATH.CONTENT.5.G.A.2–real world graphing and CCSS.MATH.PRACTICE.MP.4–model with mathematics).

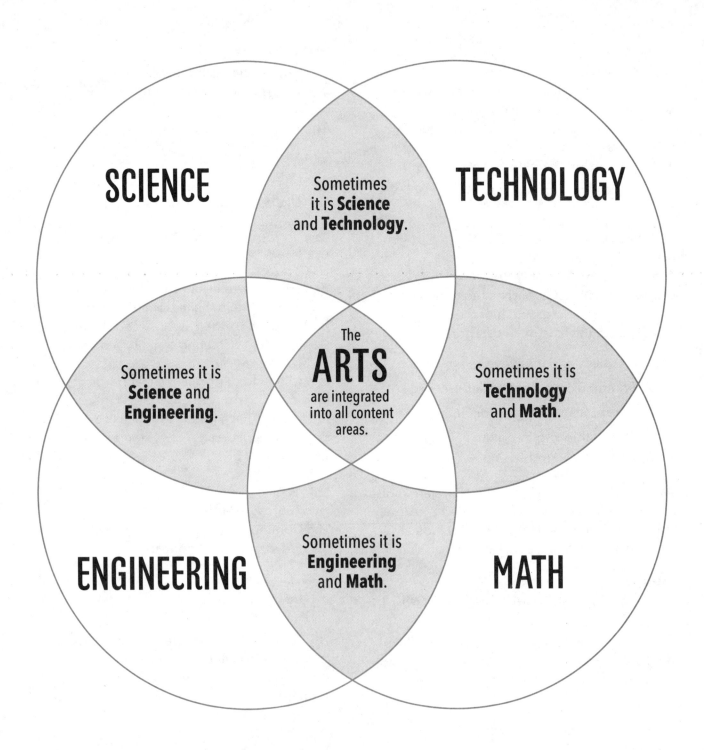

Sometimes it is all five!

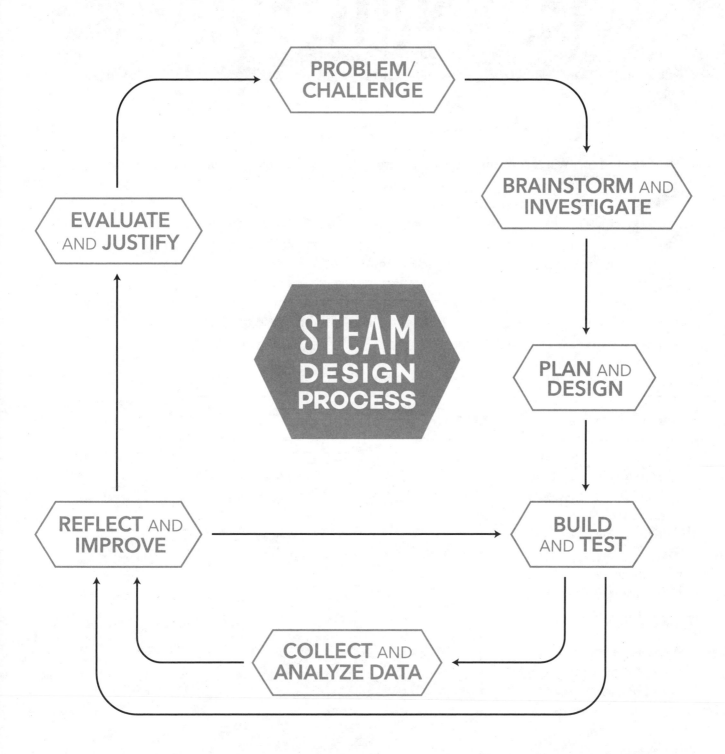

RECORDING INFORMATION IN A SCIENCE NOTEBOOK

Students will record their thinking, answer questions, make observations, and sketch ideas as they work through each design challenge. It is recommended that teachers have students designate a section of their regular science notebooks to these STEAM challenges or have students create a separate STEAM science notebook using a spiral notebook, a composition book, or lined pages stapled together. A generic science notebook cover sheet has been provided in the Appendix.

Have students set up their notebooks based upon the natural breaks in the lesson. Remind students to write the name of the design challenge at the top of the page in their notebooks each time they prepare their notebooks for a new challenge.

Pages 1–3 Background Information

- Students record notes from any information provided by the teacher during whole-group instruction.

- Students record related vocabulary words and their definitions.

- Students record notes from their own independent research, including information gathered through literacy connections and existing background knowledge.

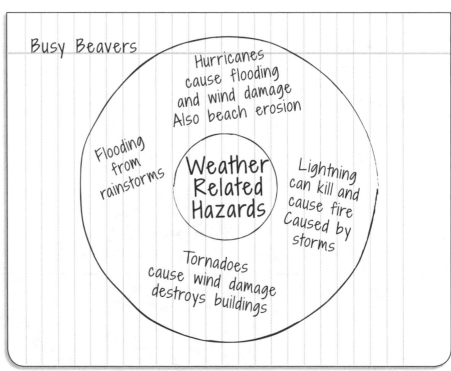

Page 1

Busy Beavers
VOCABULARY

dam – a barrier built by man or in nature (like a beaver dam) to slow down or stop the flow of water from a stream or river.

engineer – someone who designs and builds a structure or material in order to solve a problem or make something work better.

hazard – something that can be a risk or cause harm to a person, to property, or to the environment.

Page 2

Busy Beavers
NOTES FROM TEXTBOOK

p. 16 – Floods
Floods can happen anywhere but usually happen when it rains for a very long time or rains a huge amount in a very short time.

p. 17 – Drought
A drought is the shortage of water over a long period of time. It can be the cause of brush fires and wildfires.

18 – Winds
Winds that are over 40 mph can be dangerous and cause damage. They can occur during thunderstorms, hurricanes, blizzards, and tornadoes.

– Lightning
Lightning usually occurs during summer thunderstorms but can occur at any time of the year. Lightning is dangerous. It can kill people and cause fires.

Page 3

Page 4 Dilemma and Mission

- Display the dilemma and mission for students to record.

- Or make copies of the dilemma and mission for students to glue into their notebooks to use as a reference.

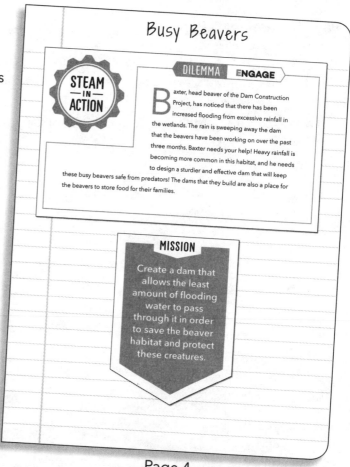

Busy Beavers

STEAM IN ACTION

DILEMMA — **ENGAGE**

Baxter, head beaver of the Dam Construction Project, has noticed that there has been increased flooding from excessive rainfall in the wetlands. The rain is sweeping away the dam that the beavers have been working on over the past three months. Baxter needs your help! Heavy rainfall is becoming more common in this habitat, and he needs to design a sturdier and effective dam that will keep these busy beavers safe from predators! The dams that they build are also a place for the beavers to store food for their families.

MISSION

Create a dam that allows the least amount of flooding water to pass through it in order to save the beaver habitat and protect these creatures.

Page 4

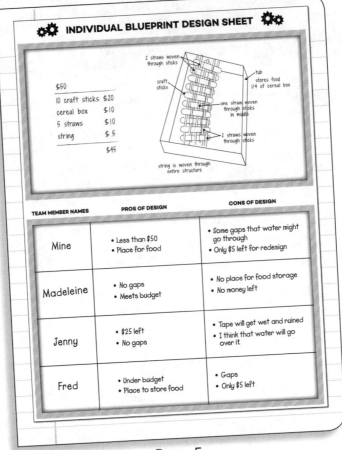

INDIVIDUAL BLUEPRINT DESIGN SHEET

$50

10 craft sticks	$20
cereal box	$10
5 straws	$10
string	$ 5
	$45

2 straws woven through sticks

craft sticks

tub stores food 1/4 of cereal box

one straw woven through sticks in middle

2 straws woven through sticks

string is woven through entire structure

TEAM MEMBER NAMES	PROS OF DESIGN	CONS OF DESIGN
Mine	• Less than $50 • Place for food	• Some gaps that water might go through • Only $5 left for redesign
Madeleine	• No gaps • Meets budget	• No place for food storage • No money left
Jenny	• $25 left • No gaps	• Tape will get wet and ruined • I think that water will go over it.
Fred	• Under budget • Place to store food	• Gaps • Only $5 left

Page 5

Page 5 Blueprint Design

● Students draw their own suggested design. Then students write the pros and cons of both their and their teammates' designs.

● Or make copies of the Individual Blueprint Design Sheet for students to complete and glue into their notebooks.

REFLECTIONS — EXPLAIN & ELABORATE

AFTER TEST TRIAL 1	How much water was in the bucket after the "flood"? Which team had the least amount of water in the bucket? Did certain materials or design features make a difference?
ANALYSIS	What changes can you make to your prototype to allow less water to flow through your dam?
AFTER TEST TRIAL 2	Did you have more or less water in the bucket after your redesign? If you could change out some of your materials, what would you use this time? Why?
ANALYSIS	What changes do you need to make in order to have less water in the bucket? Why?
AFTER TEST TRIAL 3	Which team of engineers had the dam that let through the least amount of water? What features made this prototype most effective?

Page 6

TEST TRIAL 1

Our team had almost 1 gallon of water get past our dam into the bucket. No one was successful at stopping the water from getting past their dams.

ANALYSIS

We are going to try and use craft sticks to support our straw structure. We are going to replace tape with string.

TEST TRIAL 2

We had less water after the second trial. We only lost ½ gallon of water into the bucket. We would like to change some of our "woven" straws for craft sticks to make the structure stronger.

ANALYSIS

We have just enough money to buy 2 more craft sticks. We are going to swap them for two of our straws to make our structure more stable. The water keeps bending our structure and going over it. We think adding craft sticks will help.

TEST TRIAL 3

Our final design let the least amount of water through than anyone else's, only 2 cups of water. I think that it was effective because our design did not have any gaps. We used straws to make a tight weave. We added craft sticks to provide support and stability.

Page 7

Pages 6-8 Engineering Task, Test Trial, Analyze, Redesign

- Students record analysis questions from the teacher and then record their answers. Or provide copies of the questions for students to glue into their notebooks.

- Record their reflections on the components of the prototypes that were successful and those that were not.

- Include additional pages as needed to allow students to record any notes, observations, and ideas as they construct and test their team prototype.

SUMMARY

I learned that flooding or flowing water can be a powerful force. It knocked down, went through, or went over everyone's prototypes during the first test trial. In order to succeed in slowing down the water flow, we needed to make our structure as secure and steady as possible.

Page 8

BUSY BEAVERS

S T E A M

SETTING
— THE —
STAGE

DESIGN CHALLENGE PURPOSE

Design a beaver dam to slow flooding water.

TEACHER DEVELOPMENT

Beavers play an important role in the upkeep of the wetlands environment. Wetlands are home to a variety of animal species. Wetlands absorb large amounts of water, which counteracts the effects of heavy rainfall and can prevent potential floods. Beaver **dams** can act as natural filters that keep sediment and toxins from flowing into streams and oceans. Beavers create dams in order to protect themselves from predators.

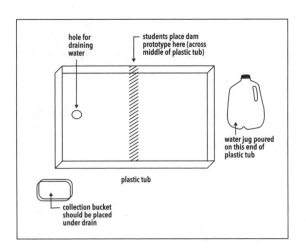

hole for draining water

students place dam prototype here (across middle of plastic tub)

water jug poured on this end of plastic tub

plastic tub

collection bucket should be placed under drain

STUDENT DEVELOPMENT

Prior to beginning this lesson, students should research and obtain information on ways in which humans and animals, such as beavers, can reduce the impact of weather-related hazards. Have students participate in a discussion about weather-related hazards. Facilitate the discussion with questions such as *What types of damage can be caused by weather-related hazards? What impact do these weather-related hazards have on the environment? How can we help design solutions to protect our environment from the weather?*

Note: Visit the website listed on the inside front cover for information about ways humans and animals can reduce the impact of weather-related hazards.

STANDARDS

SCIENCE	TECHNOLOGY	ENGINEERING	ARTS	MATH	ELA
3-ESS3-1	ISTE.2	3-5-ETS1-1	Creating #1	CCSS.MATH.CONTENT.3.NBT.A.2	CCSS.ELA-LITERACY.W.3.7
	ISTE.3	3-5-ETS1-2			CCSS.ELA-LITERACY.SL.3.1
		3-5-ETS1-3			

SCIENCE & ENGINEERING PRACTICES

Obtaining, Evaluating, and Communicating Information: Obtain and combine information from books and other reliable media to explain phenomena.

Engaging in Argument from Evidence: Make a claim about the merit of a solution to a problem by citing relevant evidence about how it meets the criteria and constraints of the problem.

CROSSCUTTING CONCEPTS

Cause and Effect: Cause-and-effect relationships are routinely identified, tested, and used to explain change.

TARGET VOCABULARY

dam

engineer

hazard

LITERACY CONNECTIONS

The Busy Beaver
by Nicholas Oldland

MATERIALS

Dam:
- craft sticks
- cereal boxes
- masking tape
- glue
- drinking straws
- yarn
- string
- construction paper
- toothpicks
- index cards
- cornstarch
- coffee filters

Flood Model:
- large plastic tub with hole in one end for draining water
- measuring cups or graduated cylinder
- gallon jug
- water collection container
- timer
- Optional: Budget Planning Chart (page 141)

NOTES

STEAM IN ACTION

DILEMMA — ENGAGE

Baxter, head beaver of the Dam Construction Project, has noticed that there has been increased flooding from excessive rainfall in the wetlands. The rain is sweeping away the dam that the beavers have been working on over the past three months. Baxter needs your help! Heavy rainfall is becoming more common in this habitat, and he needs to design a sturdier and effective dam that will keep these busy beavers safe from predators! The dams that they build are also a place for the beavers to store food for their families.

MISSION

Create a dam that allows the least amount of flooding water to pass through it in order to save the beaver habitat and protect these creatures.

BLUEPRINT — EXPLORE

Provide the Individual and Group Blueprint Design Sheets to engineering teams. Have individual students sketch a prototype to present to the other members of their team. Teams will discuss the pros and cons of each sketch and then select one prototype to construct.

Note: The budget is not set in stone. You may adjust the budget amount and material costs according to your students' level of math abilities. For example, if your students need extra practice with larger place value addition/subtraction, adjust the budget amount and materials to reflect computation in the hundreds rather than the tens.

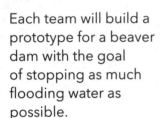

ENGINEERING TASK

Each team will build a prototype for a beaver dam with the goal of stopping as much flooding water as possible.

TEST TRIAL

Each team will place its dam prototype across the center of the plastic tub. A bucket placed under the draining hole in the plastic tub will collect the water runoff. On the other side of the tub, one gallon of water is slowly poured in and a two-minute timer is set. After two minutes, the water that made it into the bucket is measured with a measuring cup or graduated cylinder.

ANALYZE

Teams will analyze their results. Have teams discuss some of the more successful design aspects with the class.

REDESIGN

Allow teams to redesign their prototypes, including altering the original sketches using a colored pencil to show the changes they have made. The goal is to create a stronger, more effective dam. The new design must also have an updated budget sheet with the correct calculations prior to reconstructing the prototype.

HELPFUL TIPS

- After the Test Trial, have teams take a gallery walk to view other teams' designs for possible ideas to assist them in the Analyze and Redesign portions of the engineering design process.

- If teams are successful on the first try, encourage them to make their prototypes even more efficient. If it is a scenario in which this is not feasible, distribute team members to other teams to be a support for them in making their prototypes more efficient. Alternatively, at teacher discretion, move students on to the Justification portion of the lesson.

- If after the third test the final prototype is still unsuccessful, have students write how they would start over. These challenges are meant to have students build on what they originally designed. If the design proved to be unsuccessful, encourage a reflection or justification on what they would do if they were allowed to start again from scratch.

REFLECTIONS — EXPLAIN & ELABORATE

AFTER TEST TRIAL 1	How much water was in the bucket after the "flood"? Which team had the least amount of water in the bucket? Did certain materials or design features make a difference?
ANALYSIS	What changes can you make to your prototype to allow less water to flow through your dam?
AFTER TEST TRIAL 2	Did you have more or less water in the bucket after your redesign? If you could change out some of your materials, what would you use this time? Why?
ANALYSIS	What changes do you need to make in order to have less water in the bucket? Why?
AFTER TEST TRIAL 3	Which team of engineers had the dam that let through the least amount of water? What features made this prototype most effective?

JUSTIFICATION — EVALUATE

TECHNOLOGY	Use online resources to research beavers and their behaviors, including where beavers live, how they build their homes, and why they choose to create dams for their habitats.
ELA/ART	Research and create an informational brochure about beaver dams. Describe how they are built and what purpose they serve in the survival of beavers. Add step-by-step instructions for someone to build their own beaver dam.

CAN'T MISS!

S T E a M

SETTING
—THE—
STAGE

DESIGN CHALLENGE PURPOSE

Build a device that will drop a cup of water from a height of about 6 feet onto a target without spilling a drop.

TEACHER DEVELOPMENT

orce is defined as a push or a pull that changes the speed or direction of an object's motion. **Motion** is the change of the place or position of an object. Force causes motion. **Gravity** is the force that pulls objects toward other objects. Objects with the greater mass have a stronger pull of attraction. **Mass** is the amount of matter contained in an object. Because the earth's mass is so great, its gravity pulls us downward to the ground and causes objects to fall.

STUDENT DEVELOPMENT

Students need to have an understanding of the concepts of gravity, force, motion, and mass.

Lesson Idea: Read aloud the book listed in the literacy connections. Then have students use the resource listed on the website found on the inside front cover to increase their background knowledge of these concepts.

STANDARDS

SCIENCE	TECHNOLOGY	ENGINEERING	ARTS	MATH	ELA
3-PS2-1		3-5-ETS1-1		CCSS.MATH. CONTENT.3.MD.A.2	CCSS.ELA-LITERACY.W.3.2
		3-5-ETS1-2		CCSS.MATH. PRACTICE.MP.2	CCSS.ELA-LITERACY.RI.3.7
		3-5-ETS1-3		CCSS.MATH. PRACTICE.MP.5	CCSS.ELA-LITERACY.SL.3.1.C

SCIENCE & ENGINEERING PRACTICES

Planning and Carrying Out Investigations: Plan and conduct an investigation collaboratively to produce data to serve as the basis for evidence, using fair tests in which variables are controlled and the number of trials considered.

CROSSCUTTING CONCEPTS

Cause and Effect: Cause-and-effect relationships are routinely identified.

TARGET VOCABULARY

force

gravity

mass

motion

pull

push

MATERIALS

- 4 index cards
- 4 straws
- 4 clothes pins
- 4 rubber bands
- 2 pipe cleaners
- ½ of a plastic grocery bag (cut the seam of the bag to divide in half)
- 15 cm of tape
- 30 cm of string
- 1 small cup (Styrofoam or plastic)
- yardstick
- beakers or graduated cylinders
- ladder (used by teacher)

LITERACY CONNECTIONS

Gravity Is a Mystery by Franklyn M. Branley

NOTES

DILEMMA **ENGAGE**

Your mother has left you in charge of your younger brother while she runs to the grocery store. This is a big responsibility because your brother is feeling under the weather. He's all bundled up and sleeping on the couch in the living room downstairs. Your mom has left one cup with a premeasured amount of cough syrup for you to give him if he wakes up while she is gone. You are on the second floor watching your favorite television show, *Super Scientists*. If you lean over the railing, you can see your brother below. You are waiting for the show's special live announcement of the winner for a contest you entered. Oh no! Disaster! Your little brother is awake and he wants his medicine right now! But if your name appears on the screen as the winner and you miss it and aren't able to call the show, your prize will go to someone else. You decide to use the materials left over from your recent school science fair project to build a device that will allow you to drop the cup of medicine over the railing and down to your brother 6 feet below without spilling it.

MISSION

Build a prototype that will land on the target (into your brother's hands) without spilling a drop of liquid. Your teacher will show you the starting height and location. You may place the target anywhere on the ground within a 3-foot radius of the starting point.

BLUEPRINT **EXPLORE**

Provide the Individual and Group Blueprint Design Sheets to engineering teams. Have individual students sketch a prototype to present to the other members of their team. Teams will discuss the pros and cons of each sketch and then select one prototype to construct.

ENGINEERING TASK	TEST TRIAL	ANALYZE	REDESIGN

ENGINEERING TASK

Teams will construct their prototypes. They will then add 30 milliliters of water to their prototypes.

TEST TRIAL

Engineering teams will test their prototypes with teacher assistance by dropping them from a height of 6 feet. The starting point is the same for every team. Each team must measure how far the cup landed from the target as well as the amount of liquid left in the cup using beakers or graduated cylinders.

Note: Teacher will drop all student prototypes from the ladder.

ANALYZE

Teams will analyze their results. They will need to discuss some of the more successful design features with the class.

REDESIGN

Allow teams to redesign their prototypes, including altering the original sketches using a colored pencil to show the changes they have made. The goal is to get closer to the target and spill less water than in their first trial.

HELPFUL TIPS

- After the Test Trial, have teams take a gallery walk to view other teams' designs for possible ideas to assist them in the Analyze and Redesign portions of the engineering design process.

- If teams are successful on the first try, encourage them to make their prototypes even more efficient. If it is a scenario in which this is not feasible, distribute team members to other teams to be a support for them in making their prototypes more efficient. Alternatively, at teacher discretion, move students on to the Justification portion of the lesson.

- If after the third test the final prototype is still unsuccessful, have students write how they would start over. These challenges are meant to have students build on what they originally designed. If the design proved to be unsuccessful, encourage a reflection or justification on what they would do if they were allowed to start again from scratch.

REFLECTIONS | EXPLAIN & ELABORATE

AFTER TEST TRIAL 1	Which team's prototype landed closest to the target? What were the differences between the different prototypes? Did certain design features make a difference?
ANALYSIS	Which team's prototype spilled the least amount of liquid? What changes can you make to your prototype that will make it more accurate in hitting the target and less likely to spill liquid?
AFTER TEST TRIAL 2	Which team of engineers had the most effective prototype? What were the similarities and differences between the different prototypes?
ANALYSIS	What changes can you make to your prototype that will make it more accurate in hitting the target and less likely to spill liquid?
AFTER TEST TRIAL 3	Which team of engineers had the most effective prototype? Explain why you think it was the most effective.

JUSTIFICATION | EVALUATE

TECHNOLOGY	Use online resources to research gravity. Use a publishing computer program to create a brochure about gravity. Incorporate what you learned from the challenge.
ELA	You missed the announcement while you were dropping the medicine to your brother. Write a letter to the television show producers explaining what you were doing and convince them to let you demonstrate your prototype on their show. Include a detailed description of your prototype.
ARTS	Create a get well card for your brother. Include a rhyme that talks about how you delivered his medicine.

DON'T RAISE THE ROOF

STEAm

2 HOURS

TIME FOR COMPLETION

SETTING
—THE—
STAGE

DESIGN CHALLENGE PURPOSE

Design and construct a home with a roof that can withstand "hurricane-force" winds.

TEACHER DEVELOPMENT

Natural hazards are sources of danger caused by naturally occurring events such as hurricanes, floods, and tornadoes. These events can have a tremendous impact on the environment.

While humans cannot eliminate these hazards, they can reduce their impact. In this challenge, the shape and the support of the roof will determine its stability.

STUDENT DEVELOPMENT

Students will need to understand the damage wind can cause to structures such as houses. Examples of damaging winds are the winds caused by either hurricanes or tornadoes.

Lesson Idea: Place students into groups of four. Provide sticky notes and a large piece of butcher paper to each group, and have students brainstorm natural hazards and the ways humans deal with them. Students call out a hazard, write it down on the sticky note, and place it on the butcher paper. Then write an idea for how people can prevent damage to buildings caused by the hazard next to the sticky note.

STANDARDS

SCIENCE	TECHNOLOGY	ENGINEERING	ARTS	MATH	ELA
3-ESS3-1	ISTE.2	3-5-ETS1-1	Creating #1		CCSS.ELA-LITERACY.W.3.2
		3-5-ETS1-2	Creating #2		
		3-5-ETS1-3	Creating #3		

SCIENCE & ENGINEERING PRACTICES

Engaging in Argument from Evidence: Make a claim about the merit of a solution to a problem by citing relevant evidence about how it meets the criteria and constraints of the problem.

CROSSCUTTING CONCEPTS

Cause and Effect: Cause-and-effect relationships are routinely identified, tested, and used to explain change.

TARGET VOCABULARY

hurricane

natural hazard

prefabricated house

wind

MATERIALS

- empty milk carton with top cut off
- 100 toothpicks
- 10 craft sticks
- liquid glue

LITERACY CONNECTIONS

Hurricane & Tornado (DK Eyewitness Books) by Jack Challoner

Extreme Weather: Surviving Tornadoes, Sandstorms, Hailstorms, Blizzards, Hurricanes, and More! by Thomas M. Kostigen

NOTES

STEAM IN ACTION

DILEMMA ENGAGE

Hurricane Zender recently passed through the town of Windstorm, South Carolina, leaving many roofless houses in its wake. Winds caused so much damage that the mayor has come up with an action plan in response. Working with the prefabricated house company, Boxy Homes, Mayor R. U. Safer has arranged to replace the homes lost in the hurricane with prefabricated homes. The only problem is that these homes don't have roofs that will stay intact in high winds such as what Hurricane Zender brought to the town. She needs a team of engineers to design and build a home with a roof that will withstand hurricane winds.

MISSION

Design and construct a house prototype with a roof that will withstand high winds.

BLUEPRINT EXPLORE

Provide the Individual and Group Blueprint Design Sheets to engineering teams. Have individual students sketch a prototype to present to the other members of their team. Teams will discuss the pros and cons of each sketch and then select one prototype to construct.

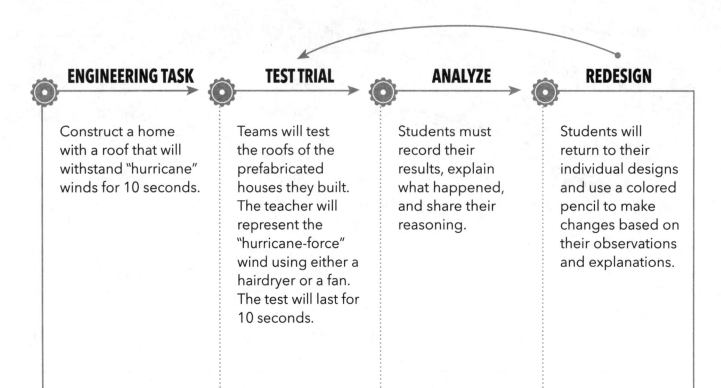

ENGINEERING TASK

Construct a home with a roof that will withstand "hurricane" winds for 10 seconds.

TEST TRIAL

Teams will test the roofs of the prefabricated houses they built. The teacher will represent the "hurricane-force" wind using either a hairdryer or a fan. The test will last for 10 seconds.

ANALYZE

Students must record their results, explain what happened, and share their reasoning.

REDESIGN

Students will return to their individual designs and use a colored pencil to make changes based on their observations and explanations.

HELPFUL TIPS

- After the Test Trial, have teams take a gallery walk to view other teams' designs for possible ideas to assist them in the Analyze and Redesign portions of the engineering design process.

- If teams are successful on the first try, encourage them to make their prototypes even more efficient. If it is a scenario in which this is not feasible, distribute team members to other teams to be a support for them in making their prototypes more efficient. Alternatively, at teacher discretion, move students on to the Justification portion of the lesson.

- If after the third test the final prototype is still unsuccessful, have students write how they would start over. These challenges are meant to have students build on what they originally designed. If the design proved to be unsuccessful, encourage a reflection or justification on what they would do if they were allowed to start again from scratch.

REFLECTIONS — EXPLAIN & ELABORATE

AFTER TEST TRIAL 1	Which team of engineers had the most effective prototype? What were the differences between the different prototypes? Did certain design features make a difference in the prototype's success?
ANALYSIS	Was your prototype able to withstand 10 seconds of "hurricane" winds? What changes can you make to your prototype that will allow it to be more successful?
AFTER TEST TRIAL 2	Which team of engineers had the most effective prototype? What were the differences between the prototypes that could withstand the wind and those that couldn't?
ANALYSIS	What changes can you make to your prototype that will make it more successful?
AFTER TEST TRIAL 3	Which team of engineers had the most effective prototype? Which team's roof was able to withstand the winds the longest?

JUSTIFICATION — EVALUATE

TECHNOLOGY	Use online resources to research hurricanes and the damages they cause as well as what humans do to reduce the impact of hurricanes. Demonstrate your knowledge by creating a slideshow.
ELA	Write a letter to Mayor R. U. Safer, describing your new prototype roof and the design, construction, and testing process you went through.
ARTS	Decorate your house to make it a part of a class cityscape of Windstorm, South Carolina.

MINI METEOROLOGISTS

STEAMm

2-3 HOURS

TIME FOR COMPLETION

SETTING —THE— STAGE

DESIGN CHALLENGE PURPOSE

Create a weather board to show your weather forecast for two days.

TEACHER DEVELOPMENT

Weather is the condition of the atmosphere at a certain place and time; it can change from minute to minute. The elements of weather are **humidity**, **precipitation**, **temperature**, **air pressure**, and wind. Humidity is the amount of water vapor in the air. Precipitation is rain, snow, sleet, or hail that falls from the sky. Temperature is a measure of how hot or cold something is. Air pressure is the amount of force placed on an object by the weight of the air. Wind is a movement of air. **Climate** is the average weather conditions in an area over time. **Meteorologists**, scientists who study weather and the atmosphere, use these elements to make predictions, or forecasts, about future weather.

Note: There are two rubrics included for you to use to provide feedback to the student teams. The weather board rubric analyzes the current weather and the two-day forecast for the weather board display. The weather forecast rubric analyzes the current weather and two-day forecast for the actual student demonstration. Artistic points have been included within the rubrics. It is suggested that the rubrics be used after the third trial.

STUDENT DEVELOPMENT

Students should know the difference between weather and climate, as well as how the two are related. Ensure that students understand the elements of weather (e.g., humidity, precipitation, temperature, air pressure, and wind) and how meteorologists use this information to make predictions about the weather.

Lesson Idea: Collect newspapers or website printouts of daily weather reports for your area. Have groups of students review the weather reports and make predictions for future weather prior to completing the challenge.

STANDARDS

SCIENCE	TECHNOLOGY	ENGINEERING	ARTS	MATH	ELA
3-ESS2-1	ISTE.2	3-5-ETS1-1	Creating #1		CCSS.ELA-LITERACY.W.3.9
		3-5-ETS1-2	Creating #2		CCSS.ELA-LITERACY.SL.3.4
		3-5-ETS1-3	Creating #3		
			Presenting #6		

SCIENCE & ENGINEERING PRACTICES

Analyzing and Interpreting Data: Represent data in tables and various graphic displays (bar graphs and pictographs) to reveal patterns that indicate relationships.

CROSSCUTTING CONCEPTS

Patterns: Patterns of change can be used to make predictions.

TARGET VOCABULARY

air pressure

climate

humidity

meteorologist

precipitation

temperature

weather

wind

MATERIALS

Use your local newspaper or the Internet to provide data for two weeks of precipitation, temperature, and wind direction for the city of your choice. Teams will use this information to determine patterns and make predictions about the weather. Provide the same data from previous years for the same area so that students can see weather patterns over time.

- poster board
- construction paper
- markers
- scissors
- sticky notes
- Weather Board Rubric (page 129)
- Weather Forecast Rubric (page 130)

LITERACY CONNECTIONS

Oh Say Can You Say What's the Weather Today?: All About Weather
by Tish Rabe

On the Same Day in March: A Tour of the World's Weather
by Marilyn Singer

NOTES

DILEMMA — ENGAGE

The WXYZ television station in Blusteryburg is losing its audience. When the station surveyed people about the reasons why they stopped watching, most of them complained that the weathercasters were often wrong when predicting the weather. Viewers were tired of dressing incorrectly or not being prepared for the last minute weather changes. They also reported that the weather forecast board needed a fresh change to make it more updated. The general manager, Ms. Electra Fied, is worried that the TV station will have to close, so she decided to hire a team of junior weathercasters to add a fresh change to the weather forecast. She will interview teams that understand weather prediction and can update the weather board with a new design.

MISSION

Create two weather maps. One for the current day and one as a prediction for the next two days.

BLUEPRINT — EXPLORE

Provide the Individual and Group Blueprint Design Sheets to engineering teams. Have individual students sketch a prototype to present to the other members of their team. Teams will discuss the pros and cons of each sketch and then select one prototype to construct.

ENGINEERING TASK	TEST TRIAL	ANALYZE	REDESIGN
Each team will create two weather boards: one that displays the current day's weather and one that displays predictions for the next two days.	Teams will display their weather boards for the class. Students will go on a gallery walk to see the displays of the other teams. They will use sticky notes to leave one positive comment and one suggestion for improvement. This will be repeated for every test trial. *Note:* Due to the nature of this activity, you may choose to only have one gallery walk. Teams can redesign their boards on their blueprint design planning sheets. At that point, you can either end the challenge or allow them to complete their boards with changes they made.	Teams will return to their own boards and review the suggestions and comments left by their peers.	Allow teams to redesign their weather display boards on their Blueprint Design Sheets using a colored pencil to show the changes they have made.

 HELPFUL TIPS

- After the Test Trial, have teams take a gallery walk to view other teams' designs for possible ideas to assist them in the Analyze and Redesign portions of the engineering design process.

- If more variety among the weather forecast boards is desired, teachers can provide the information described in the materials section for different cities so that each team provides weather information for a different city.

REFLECTIONS — EXPLAIN & ELABORATE

AFTER TEST TRIAL 1	Which team had the most accurate and current weather display boards? What positive comments did your team's boards receive? What suggestions for improvement did your boards receive?
ANALYSIS	What changes will you make to your boards based upon the feedback you received? Explain.
AFTER TEST TRIAL 2	Which team had the most accurate and current weather display boards? What did you like about them? What were some of the positive comments that were written about your boards? What suggestions were made?
ANALYSIS	What changes will you make to your weather display boards? Explain.
AFTER TEST TRIAL 3	What were the similarities and differences between the boards? Which team had the best display boards? Explain.

JUSTIFICATION — EVALUATE

TECHNOLOGY	Film a demonstration of a weather forecast using the weather board you just created. Model your forecast after a TV weathercaster's forecast. Teacher Hint: Send the videos to your local TV station's meteorologist.
ELA	Research and write about a weather-related natural disaster, such as hurricanes or floods.
MATH	Using a set of temperature data for a group of cities, create a bar graph to display the data. Write comparative sentences analyzing the data.

GALACTIC GLIDERS

1 HOUR
TIME FOR COMPLETION

SETTING —THE— STAGE

DESIGN CHALLENGE PURPOSE

Design and construct a hoop glider.

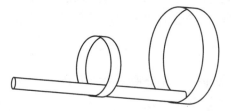

TEACHER DEVELOPMENT

This engineering challenge is a great activity for introducing students to the engineering process.

Review the Integration in the Engineering Design Challenge diagram (page 14) and the STEAM Design Process diagram (page 15) to familiarize yourself with the terms and steps associated with the engineering design process. In addition to increasing students' familiarity with the STEAM challenge process, this challenge is also an opportunity for students to investigate concrete representations of a centimeter. Do not be surprised if the first time students design their hoop flyers, they find their hoops to be much smaller than they thought.

STUDENT DEVELOPMENT

Review the steps of the engineering process with your students. This challenge is a great way to reinforce the steps and terms associated with the engineering process. If this is their first time collaborating on a project like this one, the STEAM Job cards (page 142) are useful for helping students work together.

Lesson Idea: Ask students to predict which is longer, 10 inches or 20 centimeters. Have students draw a line that is 10 inches and another that is 20 centimeters, one above the other. Discuss what they discovered.

STANDARDS

SCIENCE	TECHNOLOGY	ENGINEERING	ARTS	MATH	ELA
	ISTE.2	3-5-ETS1-1	Creating #1	CCSS.MATH. PRACTICE.MP.2	CCSS.ELA- LITERACY.W.3.1
		3-5-ETS1-2	Creating #2	CCSS.MATH. PRACTICE.MP.5	
		3-5-ETS1-3	Creating #3		

SCIENCE & ENGINEERING PRACTICES

Asking Questions and Defining Problems: Define a simple design problem that can be solved through the development of an object, tool, process, or system and includes several criteria for success and constraints on materials, time, or cost.

Planning and Carrying Out Investigations: Plan and conduct an investigation collaboratively to produce data to serve as the basis for evidence, using fair tests in which variables are controlled and the number of trials considered.

Constructing Explanations and Designing Solutions: Generate and compare multiple solutions to a problem based on how well they meet the criteria and constraints of the design problem.

CROSSCUTTING CONCEPTS

Influence of Engineering, Technology, and Science on Society and the Natural World: People's needs and wants change over time, as do their demands for new and improved technologies.

Engineers improve existing technologies or develop new ones to increase their benefits, decrease known risks, and meet societal demands.

TARGET VOCABULARY

glider

MATERIALS

- 3 straws
- tape
- 3 index cards
- ruler
- Galactic Gliders - Lifetime Pass (page 131)

LITERACY CONNECTIONS

The Wright Brothers: How They Invented the Airplane by Russell Freedman

NOTES

STEAM IN ACTION

DILEMMA ENGAGE

The CEO of the Galactic Glider Company, Mrs. Ima Soarin, wants to open a new ride at her theme park. Visitors are tired of the same old style of gliders, and she's losing customers. She wants something new that will attract tourists and boost business. Mrs. Soarin needs a new design for her gliders and wants something with a hoop. She has requested that the new glider go farther than any of her competitor's old, ordinary gliders. The team with the winning design will win a lifetime pass to Mrs. Ima Soarin's theme park.

MISSION

Build a glider that uses at least one straw and has at least one hoop.

BLUEPRINT EXPLORE

Provide the Individual and Group Blueprint Design Sheets to engineering teams. Have individual students sketch a prototype to present to the other members of their team. Teams will discuss the pros and cons of each sketch and then select one prototype to construct.

Note: Since part of the value of this lesson is in the students' comprehension of the actual size of a single centimeter, it is important to hold students to the measurements on their blueprints.

ENGINEERING TASK

Construct a hoop glider that will soar the farthest distance.

Note: Teams must have at least one straw and at least one hoop on their gliders. However, the width, length, and number of hoops are up to the teams.

TEST TRIAL

Teams will build and test their hoop gliders. If you have one student from each team line up outside at an arm's distance apart, they can all test at the same time.

Teams must measure, in centimeters, the distance their hoop gliders traveled.

ANALYZE

Students must record their results, explain what happened, and share their reasoning.

REDESIGN

Students will return to their individual designs and use a colored pencil to make changes based on their observations and explanations.

HELPFUL TIPS

- After the Test Trial, have teams take a gallery walk to view other teams' designs for possible ideas to assist them in the Analyze and Redesign portions of the engineering design process.

- If teams are successful on the first try, encourage them to make their prototypes even more efficient. If it is a scenario in which this is not feasible, distribute team members to other teams to be a support for them in making their prototypes more efficient. Alternatively, at teacher discretion, move students on to the Justification portion of the lesson.

- If after the third test the final prototype is still unsuccessful, have students write how they would start over. These challenges are meant to have students build on what they originally designed. If the design proved to be unsuccessful, encourage a reflection or justification on what they would do if they were allowed to start again from scratch.

REFLECTIONS — EXPLAIN & ELABORATE

AFTER TEST TRIAL 1	Which team of engineers had the most effective prototype? How far did that prototype glide? Did certain design features make a difference?
ANALYSIS	What changes can you make to your prototype that will make it more successful?
AFTER TEST TRIAL 2	Did your prototype glide farther this time? What were the design differences between the prototype that flew the farthest and your own prototype?
ANALYSIS	What changes can you make to your prototype that will make it more successful?
AFTER TEST TRIAL 3	Which team of engineers had the most effective prototype? What were the similarities and differences between the different prototypes?

JUSTIFICATION — EVALUATE

TECHNOLOGY	Create a video commercial featuring your prototype, the latest tourist attraction at the theme park.
ELA	Write a letter to the CEO of Galactic Glider explaining why your prototype should be the model for the new Galactic Glider.
ARTS	Create a poster advertising your prototype as the newest tourist attraction at the theme park. It will be used to entice customers walking by the entrance to come in and ride the newest Galactic Glider.

MILLION DOLLAR GEO MAN

2-3 HOURS

TIME FOR COMPLETION

S T E A M

SETTING
— THE —
STAGE

DESIGN CHALLENGE PURPOSE

Design and construct a mascot consisting of geometric figures.

TEACHER DEVELOPMENT

This lesson focuses mostly on mathematics. You will find it helpful to review with students the mathematical terms and concepts associated with this challenge. Discuss with students the different types of quadrilaterals (four-sided figures) and what shapes do not belong in that category. In second grade, students utilize various shapes to practice partitioning into halves, thirds, and fourths. For example, a square can be partitioned into two right triangles, each making up one half of the square.

While providing the background information to students, emphasize quadrilaterals. When students are manipulating and combining shapes to create new shapes, ensure that they are able to identify the newly created shape. This combining, in which they are taking two halves to create a whole, is the opposite of partitioning. As a lead in to fourth grade concepts, students will be required to draw angles and identify them in two-dimensional figures.

STUDENT DEVELOPMENT

Students must know that polygons are two-dimensional shapes that are closed and made of line segments. For example, a circle is not considered a polygon because it is not made of line segments. Investigating the resources listed in Literacy Connections, as well as the virtual shape manipulation game found on the website listed on the inside front cover, will provide a solid foundation of what polygons are and their names. *Grandfather Tang's Story* is a resource that supports the combination and manipulation of polygons to create a new figure. It is advised that, while the teacher is reading this story, the students have their own set of tangrams to manipulate.

STANDARDS

SCIENCE	TECHNOLOGY	ENGINEERING	ARTS	MATH	ELA
	ISTE.1	3-5-ETS1-1	Creating #1	CCSS.MATH. CONTENT.3.G.A.1	CCSS.ELA-LITERACY.W.3.4
		3-5-ETS1-2	Creating #2	CCSS.MATH. CONTENT.3.MD.B.3	CCSS.ELA-LITERACY.SL.3.1.C
		3-5-ETS1-3			

SCIENCE & ENGINEERING PRACTICES

Asking Questions and Defining Problems: Define a simple design problem that can be solved through the development of an object, tool, process, or system and includes several criteria for success and constraints on materials, time, or cost.

Constructing Explanations and Designing Solutions: Generate and compare multiple solutions to a problem based on how well they meet the criteria and constraints of the design problem.

CROSSCUTTING CONCEPTS

There are no crosscutting concepts for this challenge because it focuses primarily on math.

TARGET VOCABULARY

acute angle

equilateral

hexagon

isosceles

line segment

obtuse angle

octagon

parallelogram

pentagon

polygon

quadrilateral

rhombus

right angle

trapezoid

MATERIALS

- construction paper
- scissors
- glue
- pencil
- ruler
- pattern blocks
- attribute blocks
- calculator
- large poster board (students use this to glue their mascot onto)
- Million Dollar Geo Man Shapes (page 132)
- Budget Planning Chart (page 141)

LITERACY CONNECTIONS

The Greedy Triangle
by Marilyn Burns

Grandfather Tang's Story
by Ann Tompert

NOTES

DILEMMA ENGAGE

Mr. Polygon, mayor of Geometry Junction, has recently been questioned by members of his community. They want to know why they don't have a city mascot! The city council has made this project a priority and has given Mr. Polygon $1,000,000 to design and construct a mascot for Geometry Junction.

Mr. Polygon is in need of a team of designers to help him with this huge challenge. Mr. Polygon is asking all schools in the town to design a mascot. Teams may only use the approved materials, and the construction of the new mascot must use as much of the budget as possible.

MISSION

Design a mascot made of geometric shapes using only the approved materials. You must come as close to $1,000,000 as possible without going over budget. Use a variety of polygons, and label them.

BLUEPRINT EXPLORE

Provide the Individual and Group Blueprint Design Sheets to engineering teams. Have individual students sketch a prototype to present to the other members of their team. Teams will discuss the pros and cons of each sketch and then select one prototype to construct.

Note: The budget is not set in stone. You may adjust the budget amount and material costs according to your students' level of math abilities. For example, if your students need extra practice with smaller place value addition/subtraction, adjust the budget amount and materials to reflect computation in the thousands rather than the millions.

ENGINEERING TASK   **TEST TRIAL**   **ANALYZE**   **REDESIGN**

ENGINEERING TASK	TEST TRIAL	ANALYZE	REDESIGN
Teams will use their group blueprint sheets and the budget chart to construct their prototypes. They will cut and glue the shapes onto a large sheet of paper or poster board for the final design.	Each team will verify that its geometric mascot is within budget and is presentable as a mascot of the town.	Facilitate discussions comparing and contrasting the designs. Allow team members to reflect on their design compared to others and what they would do differently.	Allow teams to revise their prototypes, including altering the original sketches using a colored pencil to show the changes they have made. New designs must also have updated budget sheets with the correct calculations prior to reconstructing the prototypes.

HELPFUL TIPS

- After the Test Trial, have teams take a gallery walk to view other teams' designs for possible ideas to assist them in the Analyze and Redesign portions of the engineering design process.

- If teams are successful on the first try, encourage them to make their prototypes even more efficient. If it is a scenario in which this is not feasible, distribute team members to other teams to be a support for them in making their prototypes more efficient. Alternatively, at teacher discretion, move students on to the Justification portion of the lesson.

- If after the third test the final prototype is still unsuccessful, have students write how they would start over. These challenges are meant to have students build on what they originally designed. If the design proved to be unsuccessful, encourage a reflection or justification on what they would do if they were allowed to start again from scratch.

REFLECTIONS — EXPLAIN & ELABORATE

AFTER TEST TRIAL 1	How much of your budget did you spend? Complete a gallery walk of the prototypes so teams can reflect on their designs in order to improve. What did other teams spend on their prototypes? Who had the most expensive mascot?
ANALYSIS	What improvements or changes do you want to make to your current prototype? How much will those changes cost?
AFTER TEST TRIAL 2	Did your changes improve your prototype? How did it improve? How much of your budget did you use? What was the biggest change you made to your prototype?
ANALYSIS	How much more or less does your updated prototype cost? What future changes would you make to your prototype? Why did you change/remove/add the shapes that you did?
AFTER TEST TRIAL 3	What is the final cost of your prototype? How many polygons did your final mascot have? How many of those polygons were quadrilaterals?

JUSTIFICATION — EVALUATE

TECHNOLOGY	Utilizing the "insert shapes" function in a word processing program, create an electronic version of your prototype.
ELA	Write a justification to the mayor, Mr. Polygon, explaining why your mascot should be the one chosen. This could be in the form of a narrative, explaining how your mascot came to be, a legend, or as an informative piece that would explain the steps you followed to create your mascot.
ARTS	Create a sales pitch to convince the mayor to choose your mascot.
MATH	Use your prototype to answer the following questions: What if the mayor asked your design team for more quadrilaterals in the design than any other polygon, how would that change your mascot's form? What if he wanted more polygons that are not quadrilaterals? How would that change your design? What if the mayor decided he wanted only right angles, what would you do?

PERFECT PIRATE PLAN

stEAM

SETTING —THE— STAGE

DESIGN CHALLENGE PURPOSE

Design and build a boat that will float and carry as much treasure as possible.

TEACHER DEVELOPMENT

This is a great lesson for introducing students to the process of an engineering challenge. It is important to understand the steps involved in engineering design. Refer to the How to Use This Book section for the diagram of the STEAM design process and an explanation of each step. This challenge also applies students' knowledge of buoyancy, which is a property of matter. **Buoyancy** is an object's ability to float. The math components of this lesson involve the understanding of polygons (a closed shape), specifically a quadrilateral and a triangle.

STUDENT DEVELOPMENT

Discuss the steps of the engineering process with your students. Review the science concept of buoyancy and the math concept of polygons with your students.

Lesson Idea: Fill a large plastic tub with water. Collect 4-5 different objects, some that will float and others that will not. Have students make predictions about whether an object will float and then test each object. One object that really gets them engaged with the concept of buoyancy is an orange. First place it in tub with its peel intact. It will float. Then, try it without the peel. It sinks!

STANDARDS

SCIENCE	TECHNOLOGY	ENGINEERING	ARTS	MATH	ELA
		3-5-ETS1-1	Creating #1	CCSS.MATH. CONTENT.3.G.A.1	CCSS.ELA-LITERACY.W.3.3
		3-5-ETS1-2	Creating #2	CCSS.MATH. CONTENT.3.MD.A.2	
		3-5-ETS1-3	Creating #3		

SCIENCE & ENGINEERING PRACTICES

Asking Questions and Defining Problems: Define a simple design problem that can be solved through the development of an object, tool, process, or system and includes several criteria for success and constraints on materials, time, or cost.

Planning and Carrying Out Investigations: Plan and conduct an investigation collaboratively to produce data to serve as the basis for evidence, using fair tests in which variables are controlled and the number of trials considered.

Constructing Explanations and Designing Solutions: Generate and compare multiple solutions to a problem based on how well they meet the criteria and constraints of the design problem.

CROSSCUTTING CONCEPTS

Influence of Engineering, Technology, and Science on Society and the Natural World: People's needs and wants change over time, as do their demands for new and improved technologies.

Engineers improve existing technologies or develop new ones to increase their benefits, decrease known risks, and meet societal demands.

TARGET VOCABULARY

base
quadrilateral
trapezoid
triangle

MATERIALS

- tub
- water
- ½ bar of clay
- one roll of pennies
- scale
- Data Recording Sheet (page 133)

Note: Protect desk and table surfaces by using wax paper, newspaper, or tablecloths.

LITERACY CONNECTIONS

How I Became a Pirate by Melinda Long

NOTES

STEAM

STEAM IN ACTION

DILEMMA — ENGAGE

Oh no! You are stranded on an island in the Caribbean. How did you get here? The pirates who captured you and left you here will be back later. You have one chance to escape. You must design and build a boat using the clay you found by the lagoon. Wouldn't it be nice to take some of the treasure the pirates left on the island with you when you leave? Your boat must be able to float and carry as much treasure as possible.

MISSION

To escape the island, you must design and build a boat out of clay. It must have a base that is either a quadrilateral or a triangle and must be able to float and carry treasure.

BLUEPRINT — EXPLORE

Provide the Individual and Group Blueprint Design Sheets to engineering teams. Have individual students sketch a prototype to present to the other members of their team. Teams will discuss the pros and cons of each sketch and then select one prototype to construct.

ENGINEERING TASK

Construct a boat out of clay that will float and carry as much load (treasure) as possible.

TEST TRIAL

Engineering teams will test their boats to see how much load they can hold. Team members must weigh the load and estimate how much their boat will hold before placing the load in the boat. They will record their estimates and the actual weight measurements on the Data Recording Sheet over several trials.

ANALYZE

Students must analyze their results and compare their estimate to the actual amount of the load their boat could hold.

REDESIGN

Students will return to their individual designs and use a colored pencil to make changes based on their analysis and explanations.

 HELPFUL TIPS

- After the Test Trial, have teams take a gallery walk to view other teams' designs for possible ideas to assist them in the Analyze and Redesign portions of the engineering design process.

- If teams are successful on the first try, encourage them to make their prototypes even more efficient. If it is a scenario in which this is not feasible, distribute team members to other teams to be a support for them in making their prototypes more efficient. Alternatively, at teacher discretion, move students on to the Justification portion of the lesson.

- If after the third test the final prototype is still unsuccessful, have students write how they would start over. These challenges are meant to have students build on what they originally designed. If the design proved to be unsuccessful, encourage a reflection or justification on what they would do if they were allowed to start again from scratch.

REFLECTIONS — EXPLAIN & ELABORATE

AFTER TEST TRIAL 1	Which boat held the most treasure? What was the weight of the treasure it was able to carry? How did your prototype compare to the other prototypes?
ANALYSIS	What changes can you make to your prototype that will allow your prototype to hold more load? Does the structure of the boat need to change?
AFTER TEST TRIAL 2	Was your prototype more or less successful this time? Explain.
ANALYSIS	Did one shape work better than another? Why might that be? What changes can you make to your prototype to hold more load?
AFTER TEST TRIAL 3	Which team had the most successful prototype? What were the similarities and differences between the different prototypes? Was your prototype successful at meeting the goal? Explain.

JUSTIFICATION — EVALUATE

TECHNOLOGY	A book publisher wants to turn the details of your adventure into a book! Use a publishing program to create an electronic journal or diary describing five of the most exciting days, which should include the day you were stranded on the island and the day that you left.
ELA	Write five journal entries explaining how you were brought to the island and then escaped with the treasure. Include the steps used to construct the boat.
ARTS	Create a cover for your journal.
ART/ SOCIAL STUDIES	Create a treasure map of where you hid the treasure you weren't able to carry on the boat. Include the four main parts of a map (e.g., compass rose, key, title, and scale) on your treasure map.

PRETZERELLA

2 HOURS

TIME FOR COMPLETION

s t **E A** M

SETTING —THE— STAGE

DESIGN CHALLENGE PURPOSE

Design and construct a tower that will withstand a strong gust of wind.

TEACHER DEVELOPMENT

Pretzerella is a lesson that focuses on the concepts of engineering, art, and math. In the area of mathematics, the concept of shapes and their attributes will be necessary to complete this lesson. In addition, students will need to be able to partition shapes into parts with equal areas. The budget sheet will provide the opportunity for students to practice their fluency in adding and subtracting whole numbers.

STUDENT DEVELOPMENT

In order for students to succeed at this challenge, they will need to have a strong understanding that shapes in different categories share attributes from a larger category of shapes. For example, a rhombus and a rectangle are also quadrilaterals. Students will also need to identify various shapes and their attributes.

Lesson Idea: Have students create a foldable booklet about different shapes. Group shapes according to the number of sides and angles in each. Have students identify shapes they see around the classroom by playing a game of I Spy.

STANDARDS

SCIENCE	TECHNOLOGY	ENGINEERING	ARTS	MATH	ELA
		3-5-ETS1-1	Creating #1	CCSS.MATH. CONTENT.3.MD.D.8	CCSS.ELA- LITERACY.W.3.3
		3-5-ETS1-2	Creating #2	CCSS.MATH. CONTENT.3.G.A.1	
		3-5-ETS1-3			

SCIENCE & ENGINEERING PRACTICES

Developing and Using Models: Develop a diagram or simple physical prototype to convey a proposed object, tool, or process.

Constructing explanations (for science) and designing solutions (for engineering): Use evidence (e.g., measurements, observations, patterns) to construct or support an explanation or design a solution to a problem.

CROSSCUTTING CONCEPTS

Scale, Proportion, and Quantity: Observable phenomena exist from very short to very long periods of time.

TARGET VOCABULARY

acute angle

line of symmetry

obtuse angle

protractor

right angle

MATERIALS

- pretzel sticks
- marshmallows
- cardboard base
- fan or hairdryer (to represent wind)
- stopwatch
- Budget Planning Chart (page 141)

LITERACY CONNECTIONS

The Greedy Triangle by Marilyn Burns

If You Were a Quadrilateral by Molly Blaisdell

NOTES

STEAM — IN — ACTION

DILEMMA ENGAGE

Recently, a tornado destroyed the ancient castle belonging to Pretzerella, the princess of Pretzeltown. She is devastated by this loss and needs to begin rebuilding her castle right away. The princess sent out a royal messenger to find a team of engineers to design a prototype of the new castle. The team of engineers that makes the tallest castle that can withstand strong winds for at least one minute will be the team that designs the new castle for Princess Pretzerella. There is a budget of $20.00 to build the castle prototype. Pretzerella is fond of various geometric shapes in designs. She would like for the new castle to include at least one quadrilateral, one triangle, and one hexagon or octagon. All shapes must be labeled on the blueprint.

MISSION

With a $20.00 budget, you and your team of engineers must build the tallest castle that can withstand a gust of wind that lasts at least one minute. You must include at least one quadrilateral, one triangle, and one hexagon or octagon.

BLUEPRINT EXPLORE

Provide the Individual and Group Blueprint Design Sheets to engineering teams. Have individual students sketch a prototype to present to the other members of their team. Teams will discuss the pros and cons of each sketch and then select one prototype to construct.

Note: The budget is not set in stone. You may adjust the budget amount and the cost of materials according to your students' level of math. For example, if your students need extra practice with decimals, adjust the budget amount and materials to reflect decimal computation.

ENGINEERING TASK

Each team of engineers will follow a budget to gather the necessary materials and construct its tower prototype.

TEST TRIAL

Engineering teams will test their structures by placing them 3 feet from the "wind" (fan or hairdryer) and set the stopwatch for one minute.

ANALYZE

Each team should assess how its structure held up against the wind.

REDESIGN

Students will go back to their initial designs and make adjustments to their original blueprints, using a colored pencil to show the alterations. The goal is to improve their prototypes for the next trial. New designs must also have updated budget sheets with the correct calculations prior to reconstructing the prototypes.

HELPFUL TIPS

- After the Test Trial, have teams take a gallery walk to view other teams' designs for possible ideas to assist them in the Analyze and Redesign portions of the engineering design process.

- If teams are successful on the first try, encourage them to make their prototypes even more efficient. If it is a scenario in which this is not feasible, distribute team members to other teams to be a support for them in making their prototypes more efficient. Alternatively, at teacher discretion, move students on to the Justification portion of the lesson.

- If after the third test the final prototype is still unsuccessful, have students write how they would start over. These challenges are meant to have students build on what they originally designed. If the design proved to be unsuccessful, encourage a reflection or justification on what they would do if they were allowed to start again from scratch.

S T E A M

REFLECTIONS — EXPLAIN & ELABORATE

AFTER TEST TRIAL 1	How long did your prototype stay standing? Which part(s) of your original prototype were successful?
ANALYSIS	Which features of your prototype need to be adjusted to make the structure stronger? Do you have enough money left in your budget to purchase new materials? What changes will you make to your blueprint design?
AFTER TEST TRIAL 2	How long did your prototype stay standing this time? Did it withstand the wind longer?
ANALYSIS	What adjustments do you need to make this time? Will you need to spend more on materials to help your structure withstand the wind?
AFTER TEST TRIAL 3	Did your prototype withstand the wind? If so, how long did it stay standing? If not, what adjustments would you make to your prototype?

JUSTIFICATION — EVALUATE

ARTS	Create a scale drawing of the castle that your team constructed. Label the geometric shapes.
ELA	Write a letter to the princess explaining why your team's prototype should be chosen as the design for the new castle.
MATH	Measure the base of your tower and determine its perimeter so the princess will know how much land she needs to have available for her new castle.

THE SKY'S THE LIMIT

2½ HOURS

TIME FOR COMPLETION

SETTING
—THE—
STAGE

DESIGN CHALLENGE PURPOSE

Design and construct the tallest freestanding structure.

TEACHER DEVELOPMENT

Review the Integration in the Engineering Design Challenge diagram (page 14) and the STEAM Design Process diagram (page 15) to familiarize yourself with the terms and steps associated with the engineering design process. This challenge will increase students' familiarity with the STEAM challenge process and the associated terminology.

Additionally, this challenge includes a budget, which, if you haven't used in previous challenges, provides a great opportunity for teaching your students about this aspect of design and redesign. The mathematical concepts involved in this lesson are derived from 2nd grade measurement standards as well as 3rd grade numbers and operations standards.

STUDENT DEVELOPMENT

This is a great lesson for teaching the engineering process to students. Introduce the words **blueprint**, **design**, **budget**, **engineer**, and **prototype** to your students. Teach them how to collaborate and work as a team. To help students learn the collaboration skills required for completing these challenges, assign roles to your students. This makes the process easier to facilitate. Review the different roles described on the STEAM Job cards (page 142). Additionally, the use of a budget in this challenge teaches students about material consumption and reuse when they are trying to design or redesign their prototypes while keeping within their budget allowance.

Lesson Idea: Measurement Review- Give students a blank piece of paper. Have them draw two lines. One they estimate to be 5 cm and one they estimate to be 5 in. Tell them to label their lines with their measurements. Pair up the students. Have them compare their lines. How are they alike or different? Now give each pair a ruler. Have them draw the lines again using their rulers. Have students compare the new accurate lines to their first estimated lines to see the similarities and differences.

STANDARDS

SCIENCE	TECHNOLOGY	ENGINEERING	ARTS	MATH	ELA
		3-5-ETS1-1	Creating #1	CCSS.MATH. CONTENT.3.NBT.A.2	CCSS.ELA-LITERACY.SL.3.1
		3-5-ETS1-2		CCSS.MATH. CONTENT.3.MD.A.1	
		3-5-ETS1-3		CCSS.MATH. CONTENT.2.MD.A.1	

SCIENCE & ENGINEERING PRACTICES

Adding Questions and Defining Problems: Define a simple design problem that can be solved through the development of an object, tool, process, or system and includes several criteria for success and constraints on materials, time, or cost.

Planning and Carrying Out Investigations: Plan and conduct an investigation collaboratively to produce data to serve as the basis for evidence, using fair tests in which variables are controlled and the number of trials considered.

Constructing Explanations and Designing Solutions: Generate and compare multiple solutions to a problem based on how well they meet the criteria and constraints of the design problem.

CROSSCUTTING CONCEPTS

Influence of Engineering, Technology, and Science on Society and the Natural World:
People's needs and wants change over time, as do their demands for new and improved technologies.

Engineers improve existing technologies or develop new ones to increase their benefits, decrease known risks, and meet societal demands.

TARGET VOCABULARY

blueprint

budget

design

engineer

prototype

skyscraper

MATERIALS

- wax paper (15 cm)
- 6 twist ties
- 6 paperclips
- 5 toothpicks
- clear tape (10 cm)
- masking tape (10 cm)
- stopwatch
- meterstick
- ruler
- scissors
- Budget Planning Chart (page 141)

LITERACY CONNECTIONS

Sky Dancers
by Connie Ann Kirk

NOTES

DILEMMA · ENGAGE

Mr. I. M. Tall of Paperscrapers Inc. wants to prove the durability and versatility of his latest invention. He has created a new eco-friendly material that is very similar to the consistency of paper. He claims that he can make it without cutting down any trees. He needs your help to design and construct a prototype using his new eco-friendly material so that he can win a contract from the city of New York to build a new skyscraper. Mr. Tall warns all engineering teams that they must follow all of the guidelines and stay within budget when designing their prototypes.

MISSION

Stay within the $100 budget to construct a building prototype that stands at least 20 cm in height. It must have 3 sides, each measuring at least 8 cm in width. The structure must have a roof and use Mr. Tall's eco-friendly material (wax paper).

BLUEPRINT · EXPLORE

Provide the Individual and Group Blueprint Design Sheets to engineering teams. Have individual students sketch a prototype to present to the other members of their team. Teams will discuss the pros and cons of each sketch and then select one prototype to construct.

Note: The budget is not set in stone. You may adjust the budget amount and material costs according to your students' level of math abilities. For example, if your students need extra practice with larger place value addition/subtraction, adjust the budget amount and materials to reflect computation in the hundreds rather than the tens.

ENGINEERING TASK	TEST TRIAL	ANALYZE	REDESIGN
Teams will follow a budget when selecting materials to build the tallest freestanding structure possible. *Note:* Teams will have to purchase multiple sheets of wax paper to cover all sides of the structure.	Teams will build and test their skyscrapers. Buildings must first meet all the measurement requirements. If they meet those requirements, then engineering teams will use a stopwatch to ensure that prototypes stand by themselves for at least one minute.	Students must record their results and then explain what happened.	Students will return to their individual designs and use a colored pencil to make changes based on their observations and explanation. New designs must also have updated budget sheets with the correct calculations prior to reconstructing the prototypes.

 HELPFUL TIPS

- After the Test Trial, have teams take a gallery walk to view other teams' designs for possible ideas to assist them in the Analyze and Redesign portions of the engineering design process.

- If teams are successful on the first try, encourage them to make their prototypes even more efficient. If it is a scenario in which this is not feasible, distribute team members to other teams to be a support for them in making their prototypes more efficient. Alternatively, at teacher discretion, move students on to the Justification portion of the lesson.

- If after the third test the final prototype is still unsuccessful, have students write how they would start over. These challenges are meant to have students build on what they originally designed. If the design proved to be unsuccessful, encourage a reflection or justification on what they would do if they were allowed to start again from scratch.

REFLECTIONS | EXPLAIN & ELABORATE

AFTER TEST TRIAL 1	Which team of engineers had the most effective prototype? How long did it stay standing? What were the differences between the prototypes?
ANALYSIS	Did your prototype meet the height requirement? What changes can you make to your prototype that will make your prototype more successful?
AFTER TEST TRIAL 2	Did any more teams build a successful structure? Why do you think they did or did not? What changes do you think you should make to ensure your structure can stand on its own?
ANALYSIS	Will a higher structure mean more stability? Will a wider base mean more stability? Do you have enough in your budget to make those changes?
AFTER TEST TRIAL 3	Which team of engineers had the most effective prototype? What were the differences between the prototypes?

JUSTIFICATION | EVALUATE

ARTS	Create a billboard poster of your prototype design, adding details like color and landscaping. It should advertise office space in the latest eco-friendly skyscraper.
ELA	Success! Paperscrapers Inc. has their first contract to build a skyscraper. Convince them to use your design. Write a letter to Mr. I. M. Tall describing your prototype and the reasons he should choose your design.

ANIMALS ON THE GO

3 HOURS

TIME FOR COMPLETION

CAN BE SPREAD OVER SEVERAL DAYS

SETTING —THE— STAGE

DESIGN CHALLENGE PURPOSE

Design and construct an assistive device for an injured animal.

TEACHER DEVELOPMENT

This lesson is designed to teach empathy for injured animals and have students design assistive devices that can be related to human assistive devices. Students will need background knowledge in animal needs as well as common assistive devices that are used for humans. You can find real-life articles for your students to read and videos to watch about animals that need assistance in order to survive.

Technology has been developed in order to aid injured people through the use of special assistive devices. As technology has changed over the years, many assistive devices designed to help humans have been adapted to help injured animals. For example, the idea behind a human wheelchair has been adapted to create a type of wheelchair for dogs that cannot use their legs.

STUDENT DEVELOPMENT

Students will need to have knowledge of simple machines as well as be able to research current advances in adaptive technology. For example, the concept of a wheel and axle might support an animal that could still use its front legs but drags its back legs. Also the concept of a pulley system could potentially raise a portion of an animal to aid in movement. These simple machine concepts will support the locomotion or movement of the animal. Students will also need to understand or research the injured anatomical part of the animal they select. For example, frogs' legs move differently than a dog's legs.

Lesson Idea: In small groups, have students brainstorm how different animals move (e.g., fins for swimming, wings for flying, legs for running). Then have students discuss how a human with an injured or missing leg might get from one place to another. Listen for suggestions such as crutches, wheelchairs, and artificial legs. This is a great way for students to start thinking about how they might help an injured animal in order to complete this challenge.

STANDARDS

SCIENCE	TECHNOLOGY	ENGINEERING	ARTS	MATH	ELA
3-LS4-2	ISTE.1	3-5-ETS1-1	Creating #1		CCSS.ELA-LITERACY.RI.3.1
3-LS4-3		3-5-ETS1-2	Creating #2		CCSS.ELA-LITERACY.SL.3.1.C
3-LS4-4		3-5-ETS1-3			CCSS.ELA-LITERACY.W.3.8

SCIENCE & ENGINEERING PRACTICES

Constructing Explanations and Designing Solutions: Use evidence (e.g., observations, patterns) to construct an explanation.

Engaging in Argument from Evidence: Construct an argument with evidence. Make a claim about the merit of a solution to a problem by citing relevant evidence about how it meets the criteria and constraints of the problem.

CROSSCUTTING CONCEPTS

Cause and Effect: Cause-and-effect relationships are routinely identified and used to explain change.

System and System Models: A system can be described in terms of its components and their interactions.

TARGET VOCABULARY

adaptive technology

anatomy

MATERIALS

- stuffed animals (bear, dog, bird, frog)
- rubber bands
- chopsticks
- paper clips
- straws
- various types of paper
- tape
- plastic bottle caps
- wheels
- index cards

LITERACY CONNECTIONS

Winter's Tail: How One Little Dolphin Learned to Swim Again
by Craig Hatkoff, Juliana Hatkoff, and Isabella Hatkoff

NOTES

STEAM
— IN —
ACTION

DILEMMA **E**NGAGE

Mr. Kindheart, the director of the Critter Haven Sanctuary, takes in and cares for injured animals that are former pets or were found in the wild. Many of the injured animals can be nursed back to health. However, some animals are permanently injured and cannot move on their own. Critter Haven is a small operation and cannot afford to create adaptive devices for the animals. They need your help! Critter Haven is seeking help from local engineering teams to create adaptive devices that will assist their injured animals, allowing them to move on their own and enjoy their life at the sanctuary. Can you help?

Choose one of the following animals to create a device for:

- A bear without the use of its front paws

- A dog without the use of its back legs

- A bird without the use of one of its wings

- A frog without the use of one of its legs

MISSION

Create a prototype of an assistive device for your selected injured animal from Critter Haven Sanctuary.

BLUEPRINT **E**XPLORE

Provide the Individual and Group Blueprint Design Sheets to engineering teams. Have individual students sketch a prototype to present to the other members of their team. Teams will discuss the pros and cons of each sketch and then select one prototype to construct.

ENGINEERING TASK **TEST TRIAL** **ANALYZE** **REDESIGN**

Each team will design an assistive device for an injured animal it selected from the list. Team members will demonstrate how the device might assist a live animal, emphasizing the device's purpose and function. They will demonstrate how this device would attach to the injured animal by using a stuffed animal as a model.

Teams will construct and demonstrate their assistive devices using their stuffed animals as models. Devices must be able to attach and detach from an animal without falling apart. The teams must be able to explain the purpose and demonstrate the function of their devices.

The teacher will pass out four index cards or small sheets of paper to each team. They will be used to comment on other teams' presentations. Teams will write down two things they liked about the presentation and one question or concern they have about the device. Each team will present its device a total of three times.

After analyzing the feedback they received, teams return to their designs and make adjustments by altering the original sketches using a colored pencil to show the changes they have made. The goal is to improve their prototype for their next presentation. New designs need approval by all team members to move forward. If a device works, the team should make another type of modification, such as making it lighter or easier to attach.

 HELPFUL TIPS

- After the Test Trial, have teams take a gallery walk to view other teams' designs for possible ideas to assist them in the Analyze and Redesign portions of the engineering design process.

- If teams are successful on the first try, encourage them to make their prototypes even more efficient. If it is a scenario in which this is not feasible, distribute team members to other teams to be a support for them in making their prototypes more efficient. Alternatively, at teacher discretion, move students on to the Justification portion of the lesson.

- If after the third test the final prototype is still unsuccessful, have students write how they would start over. These challenges are meant to have students build on what they originally designed. If the design proved to be unsuccessful, encourage a reflection or justification on what they would do if they were allowed to start again from scratch.

REFLECTIONS | EXPLAIN & ELABORATE

AFTER TEST TRIAL 1	Review and reflect on the feedback your prototype received from your classmates. What did they like about your prototype? What did they have questions about?
ANALYSIS	Based on the feedback your prototype received, will you make any changes to the design? Explain.
AFTER TEST TRIAL 2	Review and reflect on the feedback your prototype received from your classmates. Were there any comments about your changes or improvements? What were they? What did they like about how your prototype worked? What did they have questions about?
ANALYSIS	Will you make any changes to your design? Explain.
AFTER TEST TRIAL 3	Review and reflect on the feedback your prototype received from your classmates. Were you satisfied with your finished prototype? If you could start again with a different animal, which animal would you build a device for and why?

JUSTIFICATION | EVALUATE

ARTS	Sanctuaries are real and they do actually take in injured animals and often run on donations. Mr. Kindheart in the dilemma represents a real person, Mr. Gary Brady. Mr. Brady runs The Critter Haven Sanctuary in Vero Beach, Florida. He is a retired art teacher and would love to receive drawings from students. Send a labeled diagram of your adaptive device to a sanctuary of your choice.
ELA	Research what a patent is and the steps to obtain one for an invention. Investigate how you would register a patent for your device.
TECHNOLOGY	Determine how solar cells, batteries, or other popular mechanical tech toys could be utilized to make your device move on its own.

FOSSIL FAKEOUT

1-2 HOURS

TIME FOR COMPLETION

S T E A m

SETTING —THE— STAGE

DESIGN CHALLENGE PURPOSE

Create three fossils that provide evidence of a marine life organism, a plant organism, and a terrestrial (land) organism.

TEACHER DEVELOPMENT

Fossils are found in rocks. They are the remains of animals and plants from a long, long time ago. When an animal or plant dies, sediment (broken down rock) will cover it, forming a mold. Over time, pressure turns the sediment into a rock. Over a long period of time, the remains of the plant or animal dissolve, leaving an imprint. This is an example of a **trace fossil**. Other times, the mold forms around the skeletal remains. This is an example of a **body fossil**.

Fossil evidence comes from different types of organisms that are classified by the environment the previously living organism came from. For example, a fossil of a sea shell indicates a **marine organism** (an animal that lived in the water). A **terrestrial organism** refers to an animal that lived on land, while a **plant organism** can be from either land or water.

STUDENT DEVELOPMENT

Students will need to know how fossils are formed and the different types of fossils as described in Teacher Development. They also need to understand that fossils are the remains of the **ancestors** of our present-day plants and animals.

Lesson Idea: Work together to come up with examples to complete a table or chart describing the types of fossils (body and trace) and characteristics (can be drawings or descriptions) of the fossil evidence for marine, plant, and terrestrial organisms.

For example, the description for the plant evidence trace fossil square could be, *A leaf fell into the mud on a riverbank. Over time, the leaf dissolved, leaving behind its imprint.*

Fossil Type	Marine Life Evidence	Plant Evidence	Terrestrial Life Evidence
Body			
Trace			

STANDARDS

SCIENCE	TECHNOLOGY	ENGINEERING	ARTS	MATH	ELA
3-LS4-1	ISTE.1	3-5-ETS1-1	Creating #1		CCSS.ELA-LITERACY.SL.3.1
		3-5-ETS1-2	Creating #2		CCSS.ELA-LITERACY.W.3.2
		3-5-ETS1-3	Creating #3		

SCIENCE & ENGINEERING PRACTICES

Analyzing and Interpreting Data: Analyze and interpret data to make sense of phenomena using logical reasoning.

CROSSCUTTING CONCEPTS

Scale, Proportion, and Quantity: Observable phenomena exist from very short to very long time periods.

TARGET VOCABULARY

ancestor   organism

body fossil   terrestrial

fossil   trace fossil

marine life

LITERACY CONNECTIONS

Fossils
by Ann O. Squire

MATERIALS

Fossil Dough Recipe:
Mix all ingredients.
- 1 cup of used coffee grounds
- ½ cup of cold coffee
- 1 cup of flour
- ½ cup of salt

Note: You can add this to the challenge and have students make the dough or make it yourself.

Fossil Making Tools:
- toothpicks
- plastic spoons
- craft sticks
- thin cardboard (e.g., cereal box)
- scissors
- note cards/sticky notes
- fossil rubric (page 134)

Note: Protect desk and table surfaces with wax paper, newspaper, or tablecloths.

NOTES

STEAM IN ACTION

DILEMMA ENGAGE

You and your team placed first in the state Science Fair. Your project about fossils had the judges fascinated. As a result, your team has been invited to attend an international event to raise money for the Museum of Natural History. While getting ready to set up a display of fossil replicas, you hear a crash! Boom! The fossil replicas go tumbling to the ground, pieces scattering everywhere! You must quickly create replacement fossil replicas for the exhibit before the big event.

MISSION

Design and construct fossil replicas, one each for a marine organism, a plant organism, and a land animal. Prototypes must be easily recognizable.

BLUEPRINT EXPLORE

Provide the Individual and Group Blueprint Design Sheets to engineering teams. Have individual students sketch a prototype to present to the other members of their team. Teams will discuss the pros and cons of each sketch and then select one prototype to construct.

ENGINEERING TASK

Construct three fossils that provide evidence of a marine organism, a plant organism, and a terrestrial (land) animal.

Note: Teams can choose to create any combination of body or trace fossils.

TEST TRIAL

Teams will display their fossil replicas in the following order: marine, plant, and terrestrial. Use note cards to label them 1, 2, and 3. Teams will use the rubric to score each other's fossil replicas.

ANALYZE

Team members must review the results of their team's rubric scores, determine the possible reason for their scores, and then develop a plan for redesign.

REDESIGN

Students will return to their designs and use a colored pencil to make changes based on their analysis of their rubric scores.

Note: The dough can be manipulated in the same day. However, it will dry and harden overnight. If you plan to extend this lesson over several days, plan accordingly so students can reconstruct their prototype prior to the dough hardening.

HELPFUL TIPS

- After the Test Trial, have teams take a gallery walk to view other teams' designs for possible ideas to assist them in the Analyze and Redesign portions of the engineering design process.

- If teams are successful on the first try, encourage them to make their prototypes even more efficient. If it is a scenario in which this is not feasible, distribute team members to other teams to be a support for them in making their prototypes more efficient. Alternatively, at teacher discretion, move students on to the Justification portion of the lesson.

- If after the third test the final prototype is still unsuccessful, have students write how they would start over. These challenges are meant to have students build on what they originally designed. If the design proved to be unsuccessful, encourage a reflection or justification on what they would do if they were allowed to start again from scratch.

STEAM Design Challenges Gr. 3 © 2017 Creative Teaching Press

REFLECTIONS — EXPLAIN & ELABORATE

AFTER TEST TRIAL 1	Which team of engineers had the most realistic prototypes? What were the differences between their prototypes and those of the other teams? Did certain design features such as the type of fossil they chose to create (body or trace) make a difference?
ANALYSIS	What changes can you make to your fossils that might give the prototypes a higher rubric score?
AFTER TEST TRIAL 2	Which team of engineers had the most realistic prototypes? Did your score improve from the previous trial?
ANALYSIS	What changes can you make to your fossils that might raise your scores?
AFTER TEST TRIAL 3	What was your final score? Did you succeed at creating three realistic fossil replicas?

JUSTIFICATION — EVALUATE

TECHNOLOGY	Use online resources to research what fossils have been discovered in your state or region. Use a publishing program to create a newspaper article about fossils found in your area.
ELA	Write a brief explanation about how fossils are formed, the different types of fossils, and describe the differences between the two main types of fossils. Include a diagram of at least one fossil.

HELP THE HIVES

STEAM

SETTING —THE— STAGE

DESIGN CHALLENGE PURPOSE

Create a model of a honeycomb as part of a larger class model of a beehive.

TEACHER DEVELOPMENT

Honeybees are an endangered species. Research has been done to learn more about these creatures and their behaviors. Hexagons are extremely important to hive building! Marcus Terentius Varro was an ancient Roman scholar whose studies included bees. He noticed that bees created hives that were circular in shape while the honeycombs inside were hexagons. His mathematical guess for why honeycombs are shaped like hexagons became known as the Honeycomb Conjecture.

The hexagonal cells that make up the hive are referred to as the honeycomb. Mathematically, hexagons are the best shapes to create a hive with because they are so compact and all the parts fit together easily, like a jigsaw puzzle. It is not important for the students to understand the different roles that the bees fill, but it is quite interesting and could be an extension to the challenge.

STUDENT DEVELOPMENT

Students will need background information on endangered species, particularly honeybees.

They will also need to know the attributes of a hexagon and how that shape relates to honeycombs, but it is important to allow them to discover that for themselves through this activity. Students will analyze, generate, and develop the patterns needed to create a model of a honeycomb that will be part of a class beehive.

Lesson Idea: Have students draw various polygons (e.g., triangle, square, hexagon, quadrilateral). They should count the number of sides and name the shapes.

STANDARDS

SCIENCE	TECHNOLOGY	ENGINEERING	ARTS	MATH	ELA
3-LS4-4	ISTE.2	3-5-ETS1-1	Creating #3	CCSS.MATH. CONTENT.3.G.A.2	CCSS.ELA- LITERACY.W.3.1
3-LS2-1		3-5-ETS1-2	Presenting #5		
		3-5-ETS1-3			

SCIENCE & ENGINEERING PRACTICES

Engaging in an Argument from Evidence: Make a claim about the merit of a solution to a problem by citing relevant evidence about how it meets the criteria and constraints of the problem.

CROSSCUTTING CONCEPTS

Systems and System Models: A system can be described in terms of its components and their interactions.

Scale, Proportion, and Quantity: Observable phenomena exist from very short to very long time periods.

TARGET VOCABULARY

circles

endangered

hexagons

polygons

squares

MATERIALS

- shoebox lid (optional)
- construction paper (cut to fit on back side of shoebox lid)
- glue
- markers
- Shape Tracing Sheet (page 135)

Note: An alternative to tracing the shapes is to use shape stamps.

LITERACY CONNECTIONS

The Magic School Bus Inside a Beehive by Joanna Cole

Everything Insects: All the Facts, Photos, and Fun to Make You Buzz (National Geographic Kids) by Carrie Gleason

NOTES

STEAM IN ACTION

DILEMMA ENGAGE

A flood has hit the town of Swarm, California. All of the man-made boxes containing beehives have been wiped out. Some of the queen bees and their drones and workers were saved. Honey is this town's main source of income. The town mayor, Mr. Sticky Sap is desperate to keep the bees alive because they are extremely important to the economy of the town. The mayor doesn't know what to do, so he is turning to you. Can your team build a honeycomb prototype to assemble with other teams to create a beehive for the queen, her drones, and workers?

MISSION

Create a honeycomb to assemble into the class beehive. Determine which shape, when repeated, will make the greatest number of cells in your honeycomb. Honeybees like patterns, so you must choose one shape that will be repeated throughout your honeycomb. Every shape must touch at least one other shape.

BLUEPRINT EXPLORE

Provide one copy of the Shape Tracing Sheet to each team. Teams must analyze the shapes and decide which shape would best meet the guidelines of the challenge. They must also decide where on the paper they will begin tracing the selected shape. Teams will need to mark their first shape with the #1 inside the shape to indicate the starting point.

Note: Have students in each team take turns tracing the shape. This will help to keep all of the students involved as they watch and wait for their turn.

ENGINEERING TASK   **TEST TRIAL**   **ANALYZE**   **REDESIGN**

ENGINEERING TASK	TEST TRIAL	ANALYZE	REDESIGN
Each team will create a honeycomb model by repeating a single geometric shape. The final honeycomb will become part of a class beehive. *Note:* The use of shoebox lids is optional to create a 3-D effect. After the final test trial, the honeycomb paper can be glued to the back of the lid. All team lids can be assembled into a large beehive.	Team members will build a prototype of a honeycomb by taking turns repeatedly tracing their chosen shape onto construction paper until the entire paper is covered or until there is no room left for a whole shape to be traced. Students will count and record the number of individual cells in their honeycomb. *Note:* To prevent second-guessing or deviation from their plan in the middle of the test trial, have teams use a marker to trace.	Facilitate analytical discussions comparing the different designs. Allow teams to reflect on their designs and the number of individual cells in their honeycombs compared to other teams.	Allow teams to discuss the redesign of their prototypes. They should discuss and determine whether to use the same shape for the next trial, but begin in a different area of the construction paper or use an entirely different shape. If they choose to use a different shape, they must still determine where they will place it on the paper to begin tracing.

 HELPFUL TIPS

- After the Test Trial, have teams take a gallery walk to view other teams' designs for possible ideas to assist them in the Analyze and Redesign portions of the engineering design process.

- If teams are successful on the first try, encourage them to make their prototypes even more efficient. If it is a scenario in which this is not feasible, distribute team members to other teams to be a support for them in making their prototypes more efficient. Alternatively, at teacher discretion, move students on to the Justification portion of the lesson.

- If after the third test the final prototype is still unsuccessful, have students write how they would start over. These challenges are meant to have students build on what they originally designed. If the design proved to be unsuccessful, encourage a reflection or justification on what they would do if they were allowed to start again from scratch.

REFLECTIONS — EXPLAIN & ELABORATE

AFTER TEST TRIAL 1	Which team of engineers made the honeycomb with the greatest number of cells? What shape did they choose? Where did they place their first shape?
ANALYSIS	What shape did each team choose? Which shape(s) worked best at creating the greatest number of cells in the honeycomb?
AFTER TEST TRIAL 2	Which shape did your team choose to create your honeycomb? Did the placement of the first shape affect the number of cells you were able to create?
ANALYSIS	What changes will you make to your prototype to increase the number of cells in your honeycomb?
AFTER TEST TRIAL 3	Which shape produced the greatest number of cells? Explain why.

JUSTIFICATION — EVALUATE

TECHNOLOGY	Use online resources to research and make a presentation about endangered honeybees and how humans can help.
ELA	Research endangered honeybees. Then create an informational article about them.
ARTS	Create a poster educating people about endangered honeybees to display next to the class model of a beehive.

YOU'RE IN THE DOGHOUSE!

S t E A m

SETTING —THE— STAGE

DESIGN CHALLENGE PURPOSE

Build a shelter for a dog to keep it safe from the heat of the sun.

TEACHER DEVELOPMENT

Environmental changes could include changes in land characteristics, water distribution, temperature, food, and other organisms. These environmental changes have an impact on living things. **Solar energy**, energy emitted by the sun, is a renewable resource and can cause great changes in our environment and the plants and animals that live there. Humans can work to design solutions to protect animals from negative environmental factors. This lesson builds upon the transfer of heat energy from the sun to various surfaces. Heat can either be **absorbed** or **reflected** based upon the surface.

Teachers should discuss with students the weather conditions and overall climate of their region and compare and contrast those conditions with a location that is vastly different. For example, compare and contrast Alaska's weather and climate with that of Florida.

STUDENT DEVELOPMENT

Students will need to research and understand the effects of the sun's energy on living things as well as its effects on weather and climate. **Weather** is the condition of the atmosphere at a particular time and place. **Climate** is defined as the average weather conditions of a particular place over a long period of time.

Note: Allow students time to use the resources found on the website listed on the inside front cover to research and interact with activities designed to further build their knowledge of weather and climate.

STANDARDS

SCIENCE	TECHNOLOGY	ENGINEERING	ARTS	MATH	ELA
3-LS4-4		3-5-ETS1-1	Creating #1		CCSS.ELA-LITERACY.SL.3.4
		3-5-ETS1-2			CCSS.ELA-LITERACY.W.3.8
		3-5-ETS1-3			

SCIENCE & ENGINEERING PRACTICES

Engaging in Argument from Evidence: Make a claim about the merit of a solution to a problem by citing relevant evidence about how it meets the criteria and constraints of the problem.

CROSSCUTTING CONCEPTS

Cause and Effect: Cause-and-effect relationships are routinely identified and used to explain change.

Systems and System Models: A system can be described in terms of its components and their interactions.

TARGET VOCABULARY

absorption

climate

reflection

solar energy

weather

MATERIALS

- pipe cleaners
- UV-sensitive pony beads
- wax paper
- tape
- foil
- plastic wrap
- construction paper
- craft sticks
- straws

LITERACY CONNECTIONS

Polar Bear, Why Is Your World Melting? by Robert E. Wells

NOTES

DILEMMA | ENGAGE

You and your family are going on a one-week camping trip this summer for your family reunion. You have prepared and packed all the necessary gear to survive in the wilderness for the week. Your pet dog, Rover, is coming along too, and according to the weather forecast, the temperature is going to be extremely high! You will need to figure out a way to keep Rover safe from overheating and too much sun exposure. There is not enough room for him to stay in the tent with you and your family, so he will need a special shelter of his own to escape the sun's rays.

MISSION

Create a shelter for Rover that will protect him from the dangers of the sun.

BLUEPRINT | EXPLORE

Provide the Individual and Group Blueprint Design Sheets to engineering teams. Have individual students sketch a prototype to present to the other members of their team. Teams will discuss the pros and cons of each sketch and then select one prototype to construct.

ENGINEERING TASK	**TEST TRIAL**	**ANALYZE**	**REDESIGN**
Each team will design and construct a pet dog using UV-sensitive beads and pipe cleaners. Then team members will construct a shelter for their dog that will protect it from the sun.	Teams will place their UV-sensitive dogs underneath their shelters in the direct sun. After 30 minutes, teams will return to check on their solar beads to monitor the effectiveness of their designs. *Note:* Introduce students to the UV-sensitive beads. Explain that they appear white when they are not exposed to UV rays. When they are exposed, the beads will change color.	Facilitate analytical discussions comparing the design features of the shelters. Allow team members to reflect on their design compared to others and what they would do differently.	Allow teams to redesign their dog shelter prototypes, including altering the original sketches using a colored pencil to show the changes they have made, with the goal of a more effective shelter.

HELPFUL TIPS

- After the Test Trial, have teams take a gallery walk to view other teams' designs for possible ideas to assist them in the Analyze and Redesign portions of the engineering design process.

- If teams are successful on the first try, encourage them to make their prototypes even more efficient. If it is a scenario in which this is not feasible, distribute team members to other teams to be a support for them in making their prototypes more efficient. Alternatively, at teacher discretion, move students on to the Justification portion of the lesson.

- If after the third test the final prototype is still unsuccessful, have students write how they would start over. These challenges are meant to have students build on what they originally designed. If the design proved to be unsuccessful, encourage a reflection or justification on what they would do if they were allowed to start again from scratch.

REFLECTIONS EXPLAIN & ELABORATE

AFTER TEST TRIAL 1	Did your shelter protect Rover's entire body from the sun's harmful rays? How do you know? Which team(s) kept their dogs protected? How do you think they did it?
ANALYSIS	What changes could you make to your prototype to better protect Rover? How did you use what you know about solar energy and environmental factors to adjust your design?
AFTER TEST TRIAL 2	After making changes to your shelter prototype, did your shelter protect Rover completely? Was there another team that was more successful this time? What did they do differently?
ANALYSIS	What changes did you make to your shelter and why? After observing Rover's shelter, what other adjustments do you think you would make to better protect Rover?
AFTER TEST TRIAL 3	Which team of engineers had the most effective prototype? Did your shelter protect Rover completely from the sun's harmful rays?

JUSTIFICATION EVALUATE

TECHNOLOGY	Record and present a video news report in which you explain the dangers of leaving pets in the heat for too long without proper shelter and care. Be sure to cite the sources used in the research for your report. Include props or visuals.
ARTS	Create a poster advertising your dog shelter. Highlight its safety features and design qualities.

A"MAZE"ING MAGNETS

STEAM

SETTING
— THE —
STAGE

DESIGN CHALLENGE PURPOSE

Design a maze that uses magnets to attract and repel a game piece through it.

TEACHER DEVELOPMENT

Everything is made of matter. Matter is made up of atoms. Atoms consist of protons, neutron, and electrons. Protons form the nucleus, or center, of the atom, while electrons spin in random directions on the outside of the atom. Sometimes the electrons will spin or travel around the atom in the same direction. When this happens, a force is created that we call **magnetism**. When an object becomes magnetized, we call it a magnet. It has the power to pull certain objects toward it. We call this a force of **attraction**. While it is a common misconception that all metals are attracted to magnets, that is not actually true. In fact most metals are not attracted to magnets. The only metals that are attracted to magnets are iron, nickel, and steel (steel is made up of iron and cobalt). Magnets can also be attracted to each other. The standards referring to magnetism refer to a **cause-and-effect relationship**. This challenge focuses on creating a magnetic attraction that occurs even though the objects do not touch. Each magnet has a south pole and north pole on opposite ends. Opposite poles of different magnets will be attracted to each other, while the same poles of different magnets will repel or push away. You will have to use strong magnets for this lesson so that the attraction can occur through a poster board.

STUDENT DEVELOPMENT

Students will need background knowledge on magnetism. Review the terminology listed in the Teacher Development and vocabulary sections. Students will apply their knowledge of magnetism when creating their mazes. They will especially need to understand that magnetic attraction can occur even though the objects are not in direct contact with each other.

Lesson Idea: Place students into groups of four. Give several magnets (different sizes and shapes) to students with only one clearly labeled with an *N* for north pole and an *S* for south pole. Challenge students to find the north and south poles of the unlabeled magnets. Then give groups a magnet and assorted objects (both magnetic and nonmagnetic). Challenge students to guess which objects will be attracted to the magnet and then make a hypothesis about what types of objects are attracted to magnets.

STANDARDS

SCIENCE	TECHNOLOGY	ENGINEERING	ARTS	MATH	ELA
3-PS2-2		3-5-ETS1-1	Performing	CCSS.MATH. CONTENT.3.OA.A.4	CCSS.ELA-LITERACY.W.3.3
3-PS2-3		3-5-ETS1-2	Presenting		CCSS.ELA-LITERACY.SL.3.1
3-PS2-4		3-5-ETS1-3	Producing Anchor Standard #4		

SCIENCE & ENGINEERING PRACTICES

Asking Questions and Defining Problems: Ask questions that can be investigated based on patterns such as cause-and-effect relationships. Define a simple problem that can be solved through the development of a new or improved object or tool.

Planning and Carrying Out Investigations: Plan and conduct an investigation collaboratively to produce data to serve as the basis for evidence, using fair tests in which variables are controlled and the number of trials considered. Make observations and/or measurements to produce data to serve as the basis for evidence for an explanation of a phenomenon or to test a design solution.

Science Knowledge Is Based on Empirical Evidence: Science findings are based on recognizing patterns.

CROSSCUTTING CONCEPTS

Patterns: Patterns of change can be used to make predictions.

Cause and Effect: Cause-and-effect relationships are routinely identified, tested, and used to explain change.

TARGET VOCABULARY

attraction

cause-and-effect relationships

contact

magnet

magnetic attraction

magnetic forces

magnetism

repel

MATERIALS

- cardboard or empty cereal boxes
- poster board
- construction paper
- craft sticks
- small magnets
- paper towel or toilet paper roll tubes
- ruler
- scissors
- glue
- tape

Note: Teams will need to create a game piece using the materials provided and then attach a magnet to it so that it can "travel" through the maze. Each team will need several magnets to place throughout the maze in order to attract and/or repel the game piece through the maze.

LITERACY CONNECTIONS

Journey to Gameland: How to Make a Board Game From Your Favorite Children's Book
by Peter Coleridge

Magnets: Pulling Together, Pushing Apart (Amazing Science)
by Natalie M. Rosinsky

NOTES

STEAM IN ACTION

DILEMMA — ENGAGE

Mrs. A. Tractor and Mr. Ree Pulsion are partners in a toy company called Attract and Repel Inc. The company specializes in creating elaborate mazes. Attract and Repel's sales are declining because their boards are old fashioned and need updating. They are advertising the need to hire more toy designers, but they want to see a sample maze to determine the quality of work. They are looking for teams of designers to show them a unique maze design that would excite customers and make them want to buy it.

MISSION

Design and build an exciting maze that uses magnets that attract and repel a game piece through the maze. Give the maze a kid-friendly theme.

BLUEPRINT — EXPLORE

Provide the Individual and Group Blueprint Design Sheets to engineering teams. Have individual students sketch a prototype to present to the other members of their team. Teams will discuss the pros and cons of each sketch and then select one prototype to construct.

ENGINEERING TASK **TEST TRIAL** **ANALYZE** **REDESIGN**

ENGINEERING TASK	TEST TRIAL	ANALYZE	REDESIGN
Build a maze that uses magnets to attract and repel a game piece through the maze. *Note:* Have teams attach their magnets to the underside of the maze.	Team members will test their maze, taking note of when the game piece is attracted to or repelled by the magnets placed throughout the maze. Have teams then try navigating the mazes of other teams.	Teams will review their maze tracks during the test trials to determine areas in need of improvement. They will want to make sure they can feel the attraction or repulsion from the magnets placed throughout their maze. These areas of attraction and repulsion should provide clues as to what direction to take in the maze.	Teams will adjust the maze paths and the placement of their magnets when necessary. Changes to the blueprint design should be done in colored pencil to indicate changes. All changes must be agreed upon by the team and approved by the teacher to move forward with them.

HELPFUL TIPS

- After the Test Trial, have teams take a gallery walk to view other teams' designs for possible ideas to assist them in the Analyze and Redesign portions of the engineering design process.

- If teams are successful on the first try, encourage them to make their prototypes even more efficient. If it is a scenario in which this is not feasible, distribute team members to other teams to be a support for them in making their prototypes more efficient. Alternatively, at teacher discretion, move students on to the Justification portion of the lesson.

- If after the third test the final prototype is still unsuccessful, have students write how they would start over. These challenges are meant to have students build on what they originally designed. If the design proved to be unsuccessful, encourage a reflection or justification on what they would do if they were allowed to start again from scratch.

REFLECTIONS | EXPLAIN & ELABORATE

AFTER TEST TRIAL 1	As you navigated your team's maze, did the clues provided by the attraction and repulsion of the magnets attached to the maze work as you designed? What theme did you create for your maze? Explain why you chose it?
ANALYSIS	What changes will you make to improve your maze? Explain. Did you make any changes to your theme? Explain.
AFTER TEST TRIAL 2	Did the changes help improve your maze? Did you observe any similarities and differences between your maze and those of the other teams? Do you need to make any additional changes? Explain.
ANALYSIS	Did your maze work as intended? How many times did you provide a choice of paths? Explain. What changes can you make to improve your maze?
AFTER TEST TRIAL 3	Did you meet the requirements of the mission? Is your maze interesting and is the design attractive?

JUSTIFICATION | EVALUATE

ARTS	Create an advertisement to promote your maze. Then design a game box for your maze.
ELA	Write a story for your maze that explains your theme.
MATH	Add directional cues to the maze that include mathematical equations. Correctly solving the equations should lead the player down the right path.

BUILDING SUSPENSE

3-4 HOURS

TIME FOR COMPLETION

SETTING —THE— STAGE

DESIGN CHALLENGE PURPOSE

Build a suspension bridge that spans a distance of at least 12 inches and holds the most weight.

TEACHER DEVELOPMENT

An understanding of balanced and unbalanced forces, as well as the strategies behind building suspension bridges will be necessary before beginning this lesson. Images of suspension bridges could be shown to students beforehand in order to help them understand the challenge better.

A **balanced force** occurs when two forces of equal magnitude act in opposite directions on an object.

STUDENT DEVELOPMENT

Students should understand that the addition of cables to bridges and the anchoring of cables on both sides can increase the load, or weight, that a bridge can support.

Note: Visit the website listed on the inside front cover for videos and additional literacy connections to review background information with students before beginning this lesson.

Lesson Idea: Have students partner up into groups of two. Give each pair of students a piece of string long enough to go across two student desks. Have students thread a washer through the piece of string. With each student holding an end of the string and with the washer laying on the desk, have students slowly stand up. They should slowly pull the string tight, trying to keep the washer in the same place on the string. If there is no movement, then the forces (students) are using the same amount of force. They are balanced!

STANDARDS

SCIENCE	TECHNOLOGY	ENGINEERING	ARTS	MATH	ELA
3-PS2-1		3-5-ETS1-1	Creating #1		CCSS.ELA-LITERACY.RI.3.5
3-PS2-2		3-5-ETS1-2			CCSS.ELA-LITERACY.W.3.8
		3-5-ETS1-3			

SCIENCE & ENGINEERING PRACTICES

Asking Questions and Defining Problems: Define a simple problem that can be solved through the development of a new or improved object or tool.

Planning and Carrying Out Investigations: Make observations and/or measurements to produce data to serve as the basis for evidence for an explanation of a phenomenon or to test a design solution.

CROSSCUTTING CONCEPTS

Patterns: Patterns of change can be used to make predictions.

Cause and Effect: Cause-and-effect relationships are routinely identified, tested, and used to explain change.

TARGET VOCABULARY

balanced force

load

span

suspension bridge

unbalanced forces

MATERIALS

- craft sticks
- glue
- string
- tape
- cereal boxes
- straws
- paper cup
- ruler
- load (e.g., pennies, marbles, metal washers)
- scale
- Permit (page 137)

LITERACY CONNECTIONS

The Brooklyn Bridge
by Elizabeth Mann

NOTES

DILEMMA ENGAGE

Oldtown, nestled on the side of a large river, is in need of some reconstruction! Its bridges were originally built for this little town when people would typically travel by foot or on horseback and pull small loads on wagons. As technology became more advanced through the years, cars, trucks, and heavy machinery were introduced into Oldtown, and the town now realizes that the old bridges are not sturdy enough to support the heavier loads. The mayor is in search of a team of civil engineers who can help design a sturdier permanent bridge and help modernize the town. The bridge prototype that spans a minimum of 12 inches and holds the most weight will win the bridge-building contract.

MISSION

Design and build a suspension bridge prototype that spans a minimum of 12 inches and holds more weight than any other team's bridge. Will your team of civil engineers win the bridge-building contract?

BLUEPRINT EXPLORE

Provide the Individual and Group Blueprint Design Sheets to engineering teams. Have individual students sketch a prototype to present to the other members of their team. Teams will discuss the pros and cons of each sketch and then select one prototype to construct.

ENGINEERING TASK	TEST TRIAL	ANALYZE	REDESIGN
Each team will design and build a suspension bridge that spans a minimum of 12 inches and holds the most weight.	Teams will build and test their bridges. Bridges will be placed on two chairs or desks spread 12 inches apart. Teams will place a cup on top of the bridge and add objects that increase the weight of the load inside the cup. Teams must weigh the load to determine how much mass the bridge can hold. They must record the mass each time a new item is placed in the cup. *Note:* Place tape on the ground to show 12 inches apart so the distance is consistent for each team.	Students must record their results and then explain what happened along with their reasoning.	Students will return to their designs and use a colored pencil to make changes based on their observations and explanation.

HELPFUL TIPS

- After the Test Trial, have teams take a gallery walk to view other teams' designs for possible ideas to assist them in the Analyze and Redesign portions of the engineering design process.

- If teams are successful on the first try, encourage them to make their prototypes even more efficient. If it is a scenario in which this is not feasible, distribute team members to other teams to be a support for them in making their prototypes more efficient. Alternatively, at teacher discretion, move students on to the Justification portion of the lesson.

- If after the third test the final prototype is still unsuccessful, have students write how they would start over. These challenges are meant to have students build on what they originally designed. If the design proved to be unsuccessful, encourage a reflection or justification on what they would do if they were allowed to start again from scratch.

REFLECTIONS — EXPLAIN & ELABORATE

AFTER TEST TRIAL 1	Which team's bridge held the most weight? What were the similarities and differences between the prototypes? Did certain design features make a difference?
ANALYSIS	What changes can you make to your prototype that might allow your prototype to hold more weight?
AFTER TEST TRIAL 2	Which team's bridge held the most weight this time? Why do you think that bridge held the most weight?
ANALYSIS	What changes can you make to your prototype to make it more successful in the next trial?
AFTER TEST TRIAL 3	Which team of engineers had the most effective prototype? What were the differences between the prototypes?

JUSTIFICATION — EVALUATE

ART	Using research from Literacy Connections and Internet sources, create a brochure about suspension bridges showcasing your design on the front panel and including information about your design.
ELA	Create a timeline showing the progression of the suspension bridge and how it has changed over the last 100 years. Include information and examples of suspension bridges around the world.

CARGO CONTRAPTIONS

2-3 HOURS

TIME FOR COMPLETION

SETTING — THE — STAGE

DESIGN CHALLENGE PURPOSE

Build a paper airplane that can carry cargo over a distance.

TEACHER DEVELOPMENT

Students will need some background on the vocabulary words in this lesson to help them understand what makes a paper airplane fly.

Gravity is the force that pulls objects or bodies toward other objects or bodies. When a plane takes off, the **thrust** (or upward push) caused by the engines allows the plane to leave the ground. In this lesson, the student is providing the thrust for his or her plane. Once the plane is in the air, the **aerodynamics**, or how the plane moves through the air based on the structure of the plane, can determine its success. Another factor that can affect the plane's success is the amount of **drag**, or force that slows down an airplane moving through the air. In addition to flying, students will need a solid understanding of how the **ballast**, or weight used to control the rising plays a part in the success of the

flight. The ballast is the weight (or cargo) added to a mode of transportation. For example, in a ship, if the ballast or cargo is all at the front of the ship, too much weight will be focused at the front, causing the ship to do a nose-dive and sink. In a plane, if the ballast is positioned at the front or back of the plane, it will not be able to fly appropriately. However, when the ballast is positioned in the middle of the plane, it will most likely travel a farther distance.

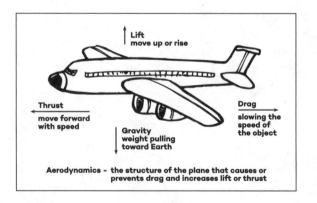

↑ Lift
move up or rise

Thrust
move forward with speed

Drag
slowing the speed of the object

↓ Gravity
weight pulling toward Earth

Aerodynamics - the structure of the plane that causes or prevents drag and increases lift or thrust

STUDENT DEVELOPMENT

In order for students to be successful in this challenge, they will need a strong understanding of the vocabulary terms in this lesson. Review vocabulary and information from Literary Connections to strengthen student understanding of important terms.

When planes fly, the cargo (e.g., luggage and people) needs to be evenly distributed throughout the aircraft. If the luggage is piled up at the back of the plane, then the plane will not be able to fly properly. The same would be true if all of the cargo was at the front of the plane.

As a quick demonstration, place a pencil on a table and place a book on top of it (like a seesaw). Slowly roll the book to the left and ask students to describe what is occurring with the book's position. (You are looking for a response that includes balanced and unbalanced forces.) Help students make the connection that if their weight provides stability or balance, it will prove a more successful flight for their planes.

STANDARDS

SCIENCE	TECHNOLOGY	ENGINEERING	ARTS	MATH	ELA
3-PS2-1	ISTE.1	3-5-ETS1-1	Creating #1		CCSS.ELA-LITERACY.RI.3.1
3-PS2-2		3-5-ETS1-2			CCSS.ELA-LITERACY.W.3.6
		3-5-ETS1-3			CCSS.ELA-LITERACY.W.3.8

SCIENCE & ENGINEERING PRACTICES

Asking Questions and Defining Problems: Ask questions that can be investigated based on patterns such as cause-and-effect relationships.

Planning and Carrying Out Investigations: Plan and conduct an investigation collaboratively to produce data to serve as the basis for evidence, using fair tests in which variables are controlled and the number of trials considered.

CROSSCUTTING CONCEPTS

Patterns: Patterns of change can be used to make predictions.

Cause and Effect: Cause-and-effect relationships are routinely identified, tested, and used to explain change.

TARGET VOCABULARY

aerodynamics

balanced forces

ballast

drag

gravity

lift

thrust

MATERIALS

- construction paper
- scotch tape
- coins or washers for weight (ballast)
- string

LITERACY CONNECTIONS

How to Eat an Airplane
by Peter Pearson

How Airplanes Get from Here . . . to There!
by Jordan D. Brown

NOTES

DILEMMA ENGAGE

Amazing Aircrafts needs your help! Companies are shipping goods at an alarming rate and the pilots are struggling to fly their planes with the extra heavy cargo loads. The pilots are making extra trips because their aircrafts can only handle so much! The CEO of Amazing Aircrafts is looking for a team of engineers to help solve this issue. They need to update their aircrafts so that they can continue to fly smoothly while carrying plenty of goods. The CEO needs a team of engineers to design an airplane prototype that can travel at least 9 feet and carry heavy cargo.

MISSION

Design and build a paper airplane that can travel a distance of 9 feet and carry more cargo weight than any other design.

BLUEPRINT EXPLORE

Provide the Individual and Group Blueprint Design Sheets to engineering teams. Have individual students sketch a prototype to present to the other members of their team. Teams will discuss the pros and cons of each sketch and then select one prototype to construct.

ENGINEERING TASK	TEST TRIAL	ANALYZE	REDESIGN
Each team will design and build a paper airplane that can travel a distance of 9 feet and carry cargo weight. *Note:* Before the challenge, use tape on the floor to mark 9 feet from the starting point, with the ending point being through the classroom door. Also mark the top third of the doorway by taping a piece of string across the doorway.	Each team will have three chances to throw its airplane with attached choice of weight. Teams may practice taping different amounts of weight onto the top of the airplane before officially testing. The airplane needs to carry the cargo 9 feet and make it through the top third of the doorway (over the string taped across the doorway).	Teams must record their results, explain what happened, and share their reasoning.	Students will return to their designs and use a colored pencil to make changes based on their observations and explanation.

HELPFUL TIPS

- After the Test Trial, have teams take a gallery walk to view other teams' designs for possible ideas to assist them in the Analyze and Redesign portions of the engineering design process.

- If teams are successful on the first try, encourage them to make their prototypes even more efficient. If it is a scenario in which this is not feasible, distribute team members to other teams to be a support for them in making their prototypes more efficient. Alternatively, at teacher discretion, move students on to the Justification portion of the lesson.

- If after the third test the final prototype is still unsuccessful, have students write how they would start over. These challenges are meant to have students build on what they originally designed. If the design proved to be unsuccessful, encourage a reflection or justification on what they would do if they were allowed to start again from scratch.

STEAm

REFLECTIONS — EXPLAIN & ELABORATE

AFTER TEST TRIAL 1	Which team's plane traveled the farthest? Did it go through the top third of the doorway? How much weight did it carry? Did certain design features help contribute to a successful flight?
ANALYSIS	What changes can you make to your prototype that will make your prototype more successful?
AFTER TEST TRIAL 2	Which team's plane traveled the farthest? Did it go through the top third of the doorway? What were the differences between the prototypes?
ANALYSIS	What changes can you make to your prototype that will make it more successful?
AFTER TEST TRIAL 3	Which team of engineers had the most effective prototype? What were the differences between the prototypes?

JUSTIFICATION — EVALUATE

TECHNOLOGY	Design a digital presentation using Prezi, PowerPoint, or SWAY to convince the CEO of Amazing Aircrafts to select your design.
ELA	Write a justification to Amazing Aircrafts explaining why your prototype should be the winning design. Be creative! Write a letter, a speech, or a song.
ARTS	Design a poster advertising your prototype.

OVER-ENGINEERED

STEAm

SETTING THE STAGE

DESIGN CHALLENGE PURPOSE

Build a Rube Goldberg machine.

TEACHER DEVELOPMENT

Rube Goldberg machines are uniquely over-engineered chain reactions.

History of Rube Goldberg:
Rube Goldberg (1883-1970) was a cartoonist that created artistic cartoons depicting inventions that took several steps to solve a problem. He received a degree in engineering from The University of California at Berkley. His cartoons made people laugh and also sparked an interest in design contests. Rube Goldberg competitions are still being held today. Rube Goldberg designs use simple machines as well as more complex machines that use an energy transfer such as a burning rope to release a reaction or a switch to turn on a toaster that moves a lever when it "pops" up. Rube Goldberg machines are valuable in helping students apply their knowledge of energy and energy transfers and actually challenge them to think of the best ways to use energy to create a complex machine.

Note: Visit the website listed on the inside front cover for additional resources about Rube Goldberg.

STUDENT DEVELOPMENT

Students will need to understand the basics of magnetic attraction and repulsion as well as the many types of energy transfers that are required in third grade science standards. This background knowledge is important as students will be applying their knowledge of those concepts in order to make a successful Rube Goldberg machine that meets all of the requirements. It will be very helpful to show them a video of different Rube Goldberg machines before having them plan.

Note: Visit the website listed on the inside front cover for a video of a Rube Goldberg machine.

STANDARDS

SCIENCE	TECHNOLOGY	ENGINEERING	ARTS	MATH	ELA
3-PS2-1	ISTE.3	3-5-ETS1-1	Creating #1	CCSS. MATH. PRACTICE.MP.4	CCSS.ELA-LITERACY.W.3.3
3-PS2-2		3-5-ETS1-2	Creating #2		
3-PS2-3		3-5-ETS1-3	Creating #3		
3-PS2-4					

SCIENCE & ENGINEERING PRACTICES

Asking Questions and Defining Problems: Ask questions that can be investigated based on patterns such as cause-and-effect relationships. Define a simple problem that can be solved through the development of a new or improved object or tool.

Planning and Carrying Out Investigations: Plan and conduct an investigation collaboratively to produce data to serve as the basis for evidence, using fair tests in which variables are controlled and the number of trials considered. Make observations and/or measurements to produce data to serve as the basis for evidence for an explanation of a phenomenon or to test a design solution.

CROSSCUTTING CONCEPTS

Patterns: Patterns of change can be used to make predictions.

Cause and Effect: Cause-and-effect relationships are routinely identified, tested, and used to explain change.

TARGET VOCABULARY

attract

balanced force

cause and effect

forces

motion

repel

unbalanced force

MATERIALS

- cups
- paper towel tubes
- plates
- craft sticks
- string
- tape

Optional:

- toy and game parts (e.g., balls, blocks, cards, dominoes, marbles, and race track parts)
- various materials students bring from home

LITERACY CONNECTIONS

Ruby Goldberg's Bright Idea
by Anna Humphrey

The Best of Rube Goldberg
by Reuben Lucius Goldberg

NOTES

DILEMMA — ENGAGE

Ms. Kon, from the Kon Structor Construction Company has a problem. Her new project requires her crew to create many twists and turns arounds bends because the owner of the property wants an unusual structure. The owner, Mr. Art Tistic, likes structures that take simple things and make them complicated by moving energy from one place to another. Ms. Kon needs your help! Design a device that works like a Rube Goldberg machine that she can use as an inspiration for her new project. The winning design team must meet all of Ms. Kon's requirements.

MISSION

Design and construct a device that operates like a Rube Goldberg machine.

Project Requirements:

1. It must have three cause-and-effect relationships related to motion.

2. It must have at least one magnet that either attracts or repels another magnet.

3. It must include a pulley, slide, or ramp.

4. It must be at least 5 feet in length.

BLUEPRINT — EXPLORE

Provide the Individual and Group Blueprint Design Sheets to engineering teams. Have individual students sketch a prototype to present to the other members of their team. Teams will discuss the pros and cons of each sketch and then select one prototype to construct.

ENGINEERING TASK	TEST TRIAL	ANALYZE	REDESIGN
Build a Rube Goldberg machine that has at least three cause-and-effect relationships related to motion; includes at least one interaction involving magnets; includes a pulley, slide, or ramp; and is at least 5 feet in length.	Teams will test their Rube Goldberg machines, noting where they need to make adjustments. There may need to be more than three trials before teams are completely successful. Teams need to be sure to meet all of the requirements for their machines to pass the test. *Note:* Instruct the students that if a team's machine stops working during their test trials, they should keep going by picking up from the next part of the machine. This will keep them focused on taking notes and collecting data for their next trials.	Teams will need to take note of where their machines stop working and then determine where to make adjustments.	Teams will use the notes that they collected during their test trials to decide how to adjust their designs.

 HELPFUL TIPS

- After the Test Trial, have teams take a gallery walk to view other teams' designs for possible ideas to assist them in the Analyze and Redesign portions of the engineering design process.

- If teams are successful on the first try, encourage them to make their prototypes even more efficient. If it is a scenario in which this is not feasible, distribute team members to other teams to be a support for them in making their prototypes more efficient. Alternatively, at teacher discretion, move students on to the Justification portion of the lesson.

- If after the third test the final prototype is still unsuccessful, have students write how they would start over. These challenges are meant to have students build on what they originally designed. If the design proved to be unsuccessful, encourage a reflection or justification on what they would do if they were allowed to start again from scratch.

OVER-ENGINEERED

STEAm

REFLECTIONS — EXPLAIN & ELABORATE

AFTER TEST TRIAL 1	Did your machine have three cause-and-effect relationships related to motion? Did it have a magnet that attracted or repelled an object? Did your machine have a pulley, slide, or ramp? Was your machine at least 5 feet in length?
ANALYSIS	Did you have any malfunctions in your machine? Do you need to adjust a component of your machine in order to complete the challenge?
AFTER TEST TRIAL 2	Did all of your adjustments work successfully? Did you meet all of the requirements of the challenge?
ANALYSIS	Do you need to make any adjustments in order to meet all of the requirements?
AFTER TEST TRIAL 3	Did your machine work successfully? Did your machine meet all the requirements of the challenge? What could you add to your machine in the future?

JUSTIFICATION — EVALUATE

TECHNOLOGY	Record your Rube Goldberg machine in action! Describe what is happening at each stage. Post the final video on the class website.
ELA	Write a story about the trip that a small character takes as he or she travels along through your Rube Goldberg machine.
ARTS	Create a Rube Goldberg cartoon strip featuring your prototype.

SHARK FRENZY

1-2 HOURS

TIME FOR COMPLETION

S T E A m

SETTING
—THE—
STAGE

DESIGN CHALLENGE PURPOSE

Design a device (such as a catapult or slingshot) that launches an object at a target 10 feet away.

TEACHER DEVELOPMENT

In this activity, students will be using unbalanced forces to move an object across a distance of 10 feet. **Motion** is when an object has a change of position. It is also a result of **unbalanced forces**, or when forces of unequal magnitude act on an object to create acceleration. A **force** is a push or a pull that changes the speed or direction of an object's motion. When we use force to move an object, we are applying more force than whatever forces are holding the object in place. Think of a tug-of-war rope. When both sides are applying the same amount of force, the

rope doesn't move. However, when one side pulls with more force than the other, the rope moves toward the side pulling with more force.

A **catapult** is a device used for throwing or **launching** objects. In this challenge, students will create a device that will launch a marshmallow 10 feet across the room toward a target. They may choose to build a catapult or even a sling shot. Either is acceptable if it meets the requirements of the challenge.

STUDENT DEVELOPMENT

Review **balanced** and **unbalanced forces** with your students. Discuss how unbalanced forces cause movement.

You may want to review the term **launch** with your students. Discuss what tools people might use to launch objects across long distances. Talk about catapults and compare them to slingshots.

Lesson Idea: Hold a tug-of-war contest. Try to balance the sides with students of equal size and strength so that there is very little movement. Invite teachers from other classrooms or parent volunteers to join one of the sides. Discuss the results with students.

STANDARDS

SCIENCE	TECHNOLOGY	ENGINEERING	ARTS	MATH	ELA
3-PS2-1	ISTE.4	3-5-ETS1-1	Creating #1		CCSS.ELA-LITERACY.W.3.3
3-PS2-2		3-5-ETS1-2	Creating #2		
		3-5-ETS1-3			

SCIENCE & ENGINEERING PRACTICES

Asking Questions and Defining Problems: Ask questions that can be investigated based on patterns such as cause-and-effect relationships.

Define a simple problem that can be solved through the development of a new or improved object or tool.

Planning and Carrying Out Investigations: Plan and conduct an investigation collaboratively to produce data to serve as the basis for evidence, using fair tests in which variables are controlled and the number of trials considered.

Make observations and/or measurements to produce data to serve as the basis for evidence for an explanation of a phenomenon or to test a design solution.

CROSSCUTTING CONCEPTS

Patterns: Patterns of change can be used to make predictions.

Cause and Effect: Cause-and-effect relationships are routinely identified.

TARGET VOCABULARY

catapult

energy

gravitational energy

gravity

kinetic energy

launch

mass

mechanical energy

potential energy

simple machine

MATERIALS

- large craft sticks
- small craft sticks
- crayons
- large piece of cardboard
- small piece of cardboard
- glue
- marshmallows ("shark food")
- masking tape
- measuring tape
- pencils
- pipe cleaners
- plastic spoons
- rubber bands
- scissors
- large plastic tub or cardboard box
- newspaper article (page 138)
- Budget Planning Chart (page 141)

LITERACY CONNECTIONS

The Big Book of Catapult and Trebuchet Plans! by Ron L. Toms

My Little Golden Book About Sharks Hardcover – June 28, 2016 by Bonnie Bader

NOTES

STEAM
—IN—
ACTION

DILEMMA · ENGAGE

Wow! You just got hired for your dream job feeding the marine animals at the local aquarium. Everyone in the community is excited about a special new exhibit. It has been designed with a tank that goes up to the ceiling. The thrilling part of this exhibit is that this unique tank will be filled with sharks! There is one big problem though, sharks are dangerous animals and they might mistake you for their meal! You have to feed them, but the tank is too high up to just throw the food up to the sharks, and if you miss, the food will fall on the people below. You will have to stand 10 feet away and launch the food into the tank. The cost of the new tank took so much of the aquarium's budget that there is only $100 left for creating a prototype that will launch food to the sharks.

MISSION

Create a device that launches food to hit a target 10 feet away and stays within a $100 budget.

BLUEPRINT · EXPLORE

Provide the Individual and Group Blueprint Design Sheets to engineering teams. Have individual students sketch a prototype to present to the other members of their team. Teams will discuss the pros and cons of each sketch and then select one prototype to construct.

Note: The budget is not set in stone. You may adjust the budget amount and material costs according to your students' level of math abilities. For example, if your students need extra practice with larger place value addition/subtraction, adjust the budget amount and materials to reflect computation in the hundreds rather than the tens.

ENGINEERING TASK	TEST TRIAL	ANALYZE	REDESIGN
Each team will construct a device that launches an object into a cardboard box or plastic tub that is 10 feet away.	Teams will test their prototypes by launching a marshmallow (shark food) into the air so that it lands inside a large plastic tub or cardboard box that is 10 feet away.	Team members compare their design and success to that of the other teams. They should discuss possible changes to their design and why they think those changes will improve their chance of success.	Allow teams to redesign their prototypes, including altering the original sketches using a colored pencil to show the changes they have made. Each redesign should have the goal of getting closer to the target. The new design must also have an updated budget sheet with the correct calculations prior to reconstructing the prototype.

 HELPFUL TIPS

- After the Test Trial, have teams take a gallery walk to view other teams' designs for possible ideas to assist them in the Analyze and Redesign portions of the engineering design process.

- If teams are successful on the first try, encourage them to make their prototypes even more efficient. If it is a scenario in which this is not feasible, distribute team members to other teams to be a support for them in making their prototypes more efficient. Alternatively, at teacher discretion, move students on to the Justification portion of the lesson.

- If after the third test the final prototype is still unsuccessful, have students write how they would start over. These challenges are meant to have students build on what they originally designed. If the design proved to be unsuccessful, encourage a reflection or justification on what they would do if they were allowed to start again from scratch.

REFLECTIONS   EXPLAIN & ELABORATE

AFTER TEST TRIAL 1	Record the distance that your marshmallow landed from the target. Which team of engineers had the most effective prototype? What were the differences between the prototypes with the closest distances to the target and those that weren't as close?
ANALYSIS	What changes will you make to your prototype to improve its accuracy?
AFTER TEST TRIAL 2	Record the distance that your marshmallow landed from the target. Which team of engineers had the most effective prototype? What were the differences between the prototypes with the closest distances to the target and those that weren't as close?
ANALYSIS	What changes will you make to your prototype to improve its accuracy?
AFTER TEST TRIAL 3	Record the distance that your marshmallow landed from the target. Did the design changes you made to your prototype make it more successful? Explain.

JUSTIFICATION   EVALUATE

TECHNOLOGY	Use online resources to learn how to adjust the arc, distance, and speed of a catapult in order to improve its accuracy.
ELA	Use the Shark Frenzy Newspaper (page 138) to write a newspaper article about the new shark tank and your prototype. The article should include a title, headings, images, and a Meet the Designer section.
ARTS	Design a sign promoting the chance to feed the sharks at Shark Frenzy! Provide information about your prototype, including a labeled diagram.

APPENDIX

My City: _____

Current Weather				Two-Day Forecast		
Precipitation		0	1	Prediction was within 2 inches	0	1
Temperature		0	1	Prediction was within 5 degrees	0	1
Wind Direction		0	1	Prediction was accurate for wind direction	0	1
Weather conditions are displayed accurately		0	1	Predictive weather conditions were displayed accurately.	0	1
Artistic touches added to enhance the display	3	2	1	Artistic touches were added to enhance the display	3	2	1

- -

My City: _____

Current Weather				Two-Day Forecast		
Precipitation		0	1	Prediction was within 2 inches	0	1
Temperature		0	1	Prediction was within 5 degrees	0	1
Wind Direction		0	1	Prediction was accurate for wind direction	0	1
Weather conditions are displayed accurately		0	1	Predictive weather conditions were displayed accurately.	0	1
Artistic touches added to enhance the display	3	2	1	Artistic touches were added to enhance the display	3	2	1

My City: _____

	3	2	1
Weather Facts (precipitation, temperature, etc.)	Weather facts are accurate.	Some weather facts are accurate.	Very few weather facts are accurate.
Descriptive Details (what/why of precipitation, temperature, etc.)	The facts were elaborated on and described in detail.	Some of the facts were described, but not enough detail was provided.	Very few details were added to the presentation.
Clear and Understandable Pace (spoken at a normal pace and clear for all to understand)	The audience can follow the forecast and understand the message being delivered.	Some portions of the presentation were unclear or too slow/fast.	Very little of the presentation was clear and understandable.

- -

My City: _____

	3	2	1
Weather Facts (precipitation, temperature, etc.)	Weather facts are accurate.	Some weather facts are accurate.	Very few weather facts are accurate.
Descriptive Details (what/why of precipitation, temperature, etc.)	The facts were elaborated on and described in detail.	Some of the facts were described, but not enough detail was provided.	Very few details were added to the presentation.
Clear and Understandable Pace (spoken at a normal pace and clear for all to understand)	The audience can follow the forecast and understand the message being delivered.	Some portions of the presentation were unclear or too slow/fast.	Very little of the presentation was clear and understandable.

⚙ **GALACTIC GLIDERS** ⚙
LIFETIME PASS

_____
PASS HOLDER'S NAME

Mrs. Ima Soarin
_____
AUTHORIZED BY

⚙ **GALACTIC GLIDERS** ⚙
LIFETIME PASS

_____
PASS HOLDER'S NAME

Mrs. Ima Soarin
_____
AUTHORIZED BY

⚙ **GALACTIC GLIDERS** ⚙
LIFETIME PASS

_____
PASS HOLDER'S NAME

Mrs. Ima Soarin
_____
AUTHORIZED BY

⚙ **GALACTIC GLIDERS** ⚙
LIFETIME PASS

_____
PASS HOLDER'S NAME

Mrs. Ima Soarin
_____
AUTHORIZED BY

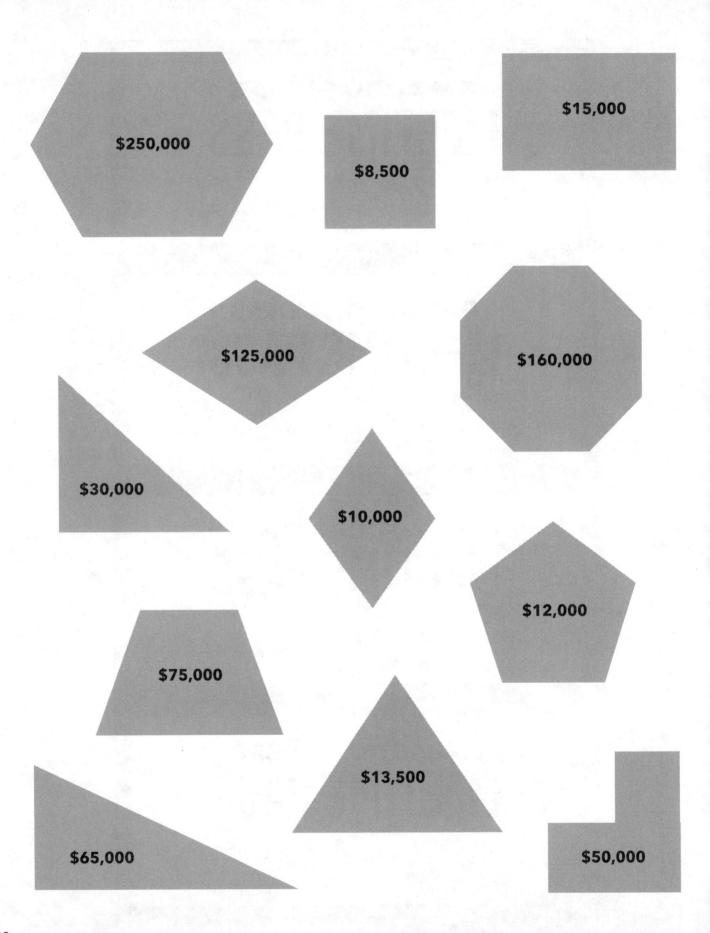

	ESTIMATED MASS	ACTUAL MASS
TEST TRIAL 1		
TEST TRIAL 2		
TEST TRIAL 3		

- -

	ESTIMATED MASS	ACTUAL MASS
TEST TRIAL 1		
TEST TRIAL 2		
TEST TRIAL 3		

FOSSIL FAKEOUT - FOSSIL RUBRIC

1 POINT	2 POINTS	3 POINTS	TOTAL POINTS
Prototype does not look like a fossil of an organism.	Can identify prototype as a fossil (either a body fossil or trace fossil) but can't determine whether it is evidence of marine life, a plant organism, or a terrestrial organism.	Prototype is easily identifiable as evidence of marine life organism, a plant organism, or a terrestrial organism.	

1 POINT	2 POINTS	3 POINTS	TOTAL POINTS
Prototype does not look like a fossil of an organism.	Can identify prototype as a fossil (either a body fossil or trace fossil) but can't determine whether it is evidence of marine life, a plant organism, or a terrestrial organism.	Prototype is easily identifiable as evidence of marine life organism, a plant organism, or a terrestrial organism.	

1 POINT	2 POINTS	3 POINTS	TOTAL POINTS
Prototype does not look like a fossil of an organism.	Can identify prototype as a fossil (either a body fossil or trace fossil) but can't determine whether it is evidence of marine life, a plant organism, or a terrestrial organism.	Prototype is easily identifiable as evidence of marine life organism, a plant organism, or a terrestrial organism.	

1 POINT	2 POINTS	3 POINTS	TOTAL POINTS
Prototype does not look like a fossil of an organism.	Can identify prototype as a fossil (either a body fossil or trace fossil) but can't determine whether it is evidence of marine life, a plant organism, or a terrestrial organism.	Prototype is easily identifiable as evidence of marine life organism, a plant organism, or a terrestrial organism.	

STEAM Design Challenges Gr. 3 © 2017 Creative Teaching Press

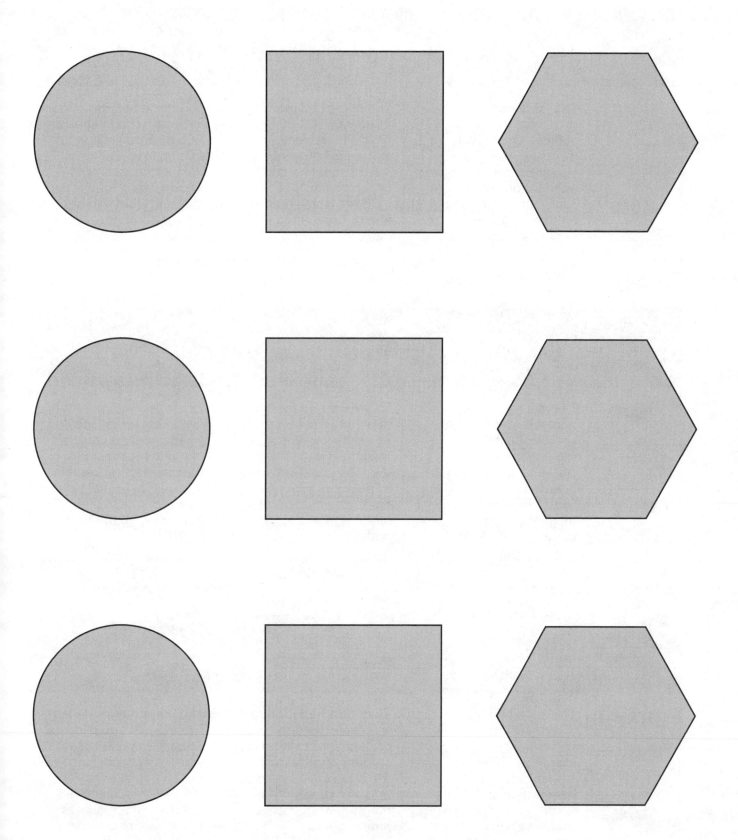

	1 Liked it, but it needs some improvement.	2 Lots of fun! I wish it was longer!	3 Absolutely A"Maze"ing!
TEAM _____ SCORE _____	The maze had less than three intersection choices. Or if it had more than three, the student approaching the intersection can't feel a "push" or a "pull" of a magnet to guide him or her to the correct path.	The maze had more than three intersection choices. At each intersection, a student approaching the intersection can feel a "push" or a "pull" of a magnet, which guides him or her to the correct path.	The maze had more than five intersection choices. At each intersection, a student approaching the intersection can feel a "push" or a "pull" of a magnet, which guides him or her to the correct path.

- -

	1 Liked it, but it needs some improvement.	2 Lots of fun! I wish it was longer!	3 Absolutely A"Maze"ing!
TEAM _____ SCORE _____	The maze had less than three intersection choices. Or if it had more than three, the student approaching the intersection can't feel a "push" or a "pull" of a magnet to guide him or her to the correct path.	The maze had more than three intersection choices. At each intersection, a student approaching the intersection can feel a "push" or a "pull" of a magnet, which guides him or her to the correct path.	The maze had more than five intersection choices. At each intersection, a student approaching the intersection can feel a "push" or a "pull" of a magnet, which guides him or her to the correct path.

- -

	1 Liked it, but it needs some improvement.	2 Lots of fun! I wish it was longer!	3 Absolutely A"Maze"ing!
TEAM _____ SCORE _____	The maze had less than three intersection choices. Or if it had more than three, the student approaching the intersection can't feel a "push" or a "pull" of a magnet to guide him or her to the correct path.	The maze had more than three intersection choices. At each intersection, a student approaching the intersection can feel a "push" or a "pull" of a magnet, which guides him or her to the correct path.	The maze had more than five intersection choices. At each intersection, a student approaching the intersection can feel a "push" or a "pull" of a magnet, which guides him or her to the correct path.

PERMIT

DESCRIPTION OF WORK:

_____

_____

_____

_____

ISSUED: _____

EXPIRES: _____

OLDTOWN
BUILDING DEPARTMENT

SEAL OF APPROVAL
OLDTOWN
BUILDING DEPT.

_____
CHIEF CIVIL ENGINEER

_____
MAYOR

EXTRA! EXTRA!

_____
Title

Written by: _____

_____

_____

_____

_____

_____

| Prototype Image |

_____

_____

| Shark Tank Image | Meet the Designers |

INDIVIDUAL BLUEPRINT DESIGN SHEET

TEAM MEMBER NAMES	PROS OF DESIGN	CONS OF DESIGN

TEAM REASONING

TEACHER APPROVAL:

⚙ BUDGET PLANNING CHART ⚙

TITLE:

MATERIALS	COST	1st TEST TRIAL		2nd TEST TRIAL		3rd TEST TRIAL	
		ITEM(S)	AMOUNT	ITEM(S)	AMOUNT	ITEM(S)	AMOUNT
TOTAL COST:							

Assigning students roles, or jobs, often helps them to collaborate by giving them some guidelines to follow. As they become more practiced at problem solving, communicating, and collaborating, they will fall into these roles naturally. In the meantime, we've provided these cards, which describe each job on their collaborative team.

Construction Specialist

Description: This person is the one whose design was chosen. This person builds the prototype and is responsible for ensuring that the prototype follows the design parameters exactly.

Material Resource Officer

Description: This person is in charge of measuring, cutting, and procuring materials for the prototypes. This person assists the construction specialist by getting materials ready and assisting in construction.

Engineering Supervisor

Description: This person is the team leader. This person assists all other team members as needed. This person acts as spokesperson for the team. This person will test the team's prototype.

Administrative Contractor

Description: This person is responsible for overseeing the construction specialist. This person must measure or otherwise ensure that prototype construction matches the blueprint design.

(Use only with groups of five.)

Accounts Manager

Description: This person holds the purse strings, keeps the team's finance records (budget sheet), and pays for all materials. This person assists the engineering supervisor with testing and recording all data.

INVENTOR'S NOTEBOOK

_____
Name

STEAM MONEY

ONE DOLLAR $1
ONE DOLLAR $1
ONE DOLLAR $1
ONE DOLLAR $1

ONE DOLLAR $1
ONE DOLLAR $1
ONE DOLLAR $1
ONE DOLLAR $1

ONE DOLLAR $1
ONE DOLLAR $1
ONE DOLLAR $1
ONE DOLLAR $1

FIVE DOLLARS $5
FIVE DOLLARS $5
FIVE DOLLARS $5
FIVE DOLLARS $5

FIVE DOLLARS $5
FIVE DOLLARS $5
FIVE DOLLARS $5
FIVE DOLLARS $5

FIVE DOLLARS $5
FIVE DOLLARS $5
FIVE DOLLARS $5
FIVE DOLLARS $5

STEAM MONEY

25	TWENTY-FIVE DOLLARS $	25	TWENTY-FIVE DOLLARS $	25	TWENTY-FIVE DOLLARS $	25	TWENTY-FIVE DOLLARS $
$	$25	25	$	$25	25	$	$25	25	$	$25	25

$25 $25 $25 $25

$25 $25 $25 $25

$50 $50 $50 $50

$50 $50 $50 $50

$50 $50 $50 $50

TWENTY-FIVE DOLLARS — FIFTY DOLLARS

STEAM DESIGN CHALLENGES TEAM RUBRIC

	EXEMPLARY	PROFICIENT	PROGRESSING	BEGINNING
DESIGN	Team members reach consensus as to which prototype to construct. They complete team blueprint design sheet in which they include their reasons for selecting the team prototype. They include a written explanation to compare and contrast the prototypes they sketched individually. Prototype is constructed according to specifications in the team blueprint design.	Team members reach consensus as to which prototype to construct. They include their reasons for selecting the prototype but do not include a written explanation to compare and contrast the prototypes they sketched individually. Prototype is constructed according to the specifications in the team blueprint design.	Team members reach consensus as to which prototype to construct. They include their reasons for selecting the prototype but do not include a written explanation to compare and contrast the prototypes they sketched individually. Prototype is not constructed according to the specifications of the blueprint design.	Team members reach consensus as to which prototype to construct. They do not include either their reasons for selecting the prototype or a written explanation to compare and contrast the prototypes they sketched. Prototype is constructed.
TEST	Teams test their prototype. They record observations that align with the design challenge. They make note of any unique design flaws.	Teams test their prototype and record observations that align with the design challenge.	Teams test their prototype. They record observations that do not align with the design challenge.	Teams test their prototype. They do not record observations.

STEAM DESIGN CHALLENGES TEAM RUBRIC

	EXEMPLARY	PROFICIENT	PROGRESSING	BEGINNING
ANALYZE	Team members participate in an analytic discussion about their testing and observations. They reflect on their design as compared to at least three other teams. They discuss their intended redesign steps, defending their reasoning in their discussion.	Team members participate in an analytic discussion about their testing and observations. They reflect on their design as compared to at least two other teams. They discuss their intended redesign steps.	Team members participate in an analytic discussion about their testing and observations, comparing their design with at least one other team's. They discuss their intended redesign steps.	Team members participate in an analytic discussion about their testing but do not compare their design with another team's. They discuss their intended redesign steps.
REDESIGN	Team redesigns its prototype. Original sketch is altered using a colored pencil to illustrate changes made with supporting reasons.	Team redesigns its prototype. Original sketch is altered using a colored pencil to illustrate changes made.	Team redesigns its prototype. Original sketch is altered to illustrate changes made.	Team redesigns its prototype.
EVALUATE	Team completes a justification activity. Team reflects and makes meaningful connections to the science standards as well as to two of the other STEAM standards addressed in the lesson.	Team completes a justification activity. Team reflects and makes meaningful connections to the science standards as well as to one of the other STEAM standards addressed in the lesson.	Team completes a justification activity. Team reflects and makes meaningful connections to the science standards addressed in the lesson.	Team completes a justification activity. Team makes no connection to the science standards addressed in the lesson.

GLOSSARY

WORD	DEFINITION
absorption	The process of taking in and holding.
acute angle	An angle measuring less than 90 degrees.
adaptation	A physical feature or a behavior that helps an organism survive in its habitat.
adaptive technology	A piece of equipment used to improve the life of a person with a disability.
aerodynamics	Dealing with the motion of air and other gases and with the forces acting on bodies in motion through these gases.
air pressure	The amount of force placed on an object by the weight of the air.
anatomy	A science that studies the structure of living things.
attraction	The act or power of drawing things together.
balanced force	Two forces of equal magnitude acting in opposite directions on an object.
ballast	Heavy material used to control the rising of a balloon or ship.
base	A thing or part on which something rests; bottom. A line or surface of a geometric figure upon which an altitude is or is thought to be constructed.
blueprint	A photographic print made with white lines on a blue background and used for copying maps and building plans.
body fossil	Fossil formed from the remains of dead animals and plants, usually teeth, bones, shells, woody trunks, branches, and stems.
buoyancy	The power of rising and floating in water or in air.
catapult	A device for launching or throwing objects.
cause-and-effect relationship	A relationship in which one event (the cause) makes another event (the effect) happen.
client	A person who uses the professional advice or services of another.
climate	The average weather conditions in an area over a long period of time.
dam	A barrier to hold back a flow of water.
design	A plan. A sketch or model.
drag	The force slowing down an airplane moving through the air.
endangered	A species at risk of extinction.

STEAM Design Challenges Gr. 3 © 2017 Creative Teaching Press

WORD	DEFINITION
energy	The ability to cause change or do work.
engineer	To plan or build. A person who specializes in engineering.
equilateral	A shape having all sides of equal length.
force	A push or pull that changes the speed or direction of an object's motion.
fossil	The preserved traces and remains of an organism that lived long ago.
glider	An aircraft without an engine that glides on air current.
gravitational energy	The energy an object has because of its high position compared to a lower position.
gravity	The force that pulls objects or bodies toward other objects or bodies.
humidity	The amount of water vapor in the air.
hurricane	A tropical cyclone with winds of 74 miles per hour or greater, usually with rain, thunder, and lightning.
isosceles	A triangle having two sides of equal length.
kinetic energy	The energy that an object has because it is moving.
launch	To throw or send off with force.
lift	The force that opposes the pull of gravity as on an airplane wing.
line of symmetry	The imaginary line that divides an image in half with both halves matching exactly.
line segment	A part of a straight line included between two points.
load	A mass or weight supported by something.
locomotion	Movement or the act of moving from place to place.
magnetism	An invisible force or field with the power to attract iron and certain metals in electric currents and magnets.
magnetic attraction	The force that draws the unlike poles of two magnets together.
magnetic energy	The energy within a magnetic field. This energy results in metals either repelling or attracting each other.
magnetic forces	The attraction or repulsion between electrically charged particles.
marine life	Animals and plants that live in the ocean.
mass	The amount of matter in an object.
mechanical energy	The energy an object has because of its motion and position.
meteorologist	A scientist who specializes in meteorology, which is the science related to the atmosphere, weather, and weather forecasting.

WORD	DEFINITION
meteorology	The science related to the atmosphere, weather, and weather forecasting.
motion	The act of changing place or position.
natural hazard	A source of danger caused by naturally occurring events such as earthquakes, landslides, floods, extreme temperatures, and hurricanes.
obtuse angle	An angle measuring more than 90 degrees.
organism	Any living thing.
plant organism	A multicellular organism that contains chloroplast and uses light to undergo photosynthesis for energy.
potential energy	The energy in an object based on its position in relation to other objects.
precipitation	Rain, snow, sleet, or hail that falls from the sky.
prediction	The act of figuring out and telling beforehand.
prefabricated house	A house that is constructed of pieces that were built in a factory and then shipped and assembled at its final destination.
protractor	An instrument used for drawing and measuring angles.
pull	To use force on to cause movement toward the force or to force apart.
push	To press against with force to move away. To force forward, downward, or outward.
reflection	What happens when light waves bounce off a surface.
repel	To drive away or apart.
right angle	An angle measuring 90 degrees.
simple machine	A device that changes a force to make work easier
solar energy	Energy emitted by the sun.
span	The spread or distance from one support to another.
suspension bridge	A bridge that has its roadway suspended from two or more cables.
temperature	A measure of how hot or cold something is.
terrestrial	Of or relating to the earth or its people. Living or growing on land.
thrust	A forward or upward push.
trace fossil	A fossil of a footprint, trail, burrow, or other trace of an animal.
unbalanced force	Forces of unequal magnitude acting on an object to create acceleration.
weather	The condition of the atmosphere at a certain place and time.

STEAM Design Challenges Gr. 3 © 2017 Creative Teaching Press

BIBLIOGRAPHY

"All About Magnetism and How It Works." Easy Science for Kids. Accessed July 16, 2016. http://easyscienceforkids.com/all-about-magnetism/.

"All About Simple Machines: Types and Functions." Easy Science for Kids. Accessed August 19, 2016. http://easyscienceforkids.com/all-about-simple-machines/.

"Assistive Devices for Animals." Ann Arbor Animal Hospital. Accessed August 19, 2016. http://annarboranimalhospital.com/2015/04/assistive-devices-for-animals/.

Bailey, Kevin. Fun Paper Airplanes. Accessed June 23, 2016. http://www.funpaperairplanes.com/learn_about_flight.html.

"Coffee Ground 'Fossils.'" Kids GeoZone. California Geological Survey. Accessed August 2, 2016. http://www.conservation.ca.gov/cgs/information/kids_geozone/Pages/fossil.aspx.

"Critter Haven of Vero Beach." Vero Beach.com. Accessed August 19, 2016. http://www.verobeach.com/vero-beach-directories/critter-haven-of-vero-beach.

Darby, Gary. "Catapult Simulator." DelphiForFun.org. Accessed July 23, 2016. http://delphiforfun.org/programs/catapult.htm.

"Developing Geometry Understandings with Tangrams." Illuminations. National Council of Teachers of Mathematics. Accessed June 30, 2016. https://illuminations.nctm.org/Activity.aspx?id=6384.

"Force and Motion: Facts." Science Trek. Idaho Public Television. Accessed August 5, 2016. http://idahoptv.org/sciencetrek/topics/force_and_motion/facts.cfm.

Frank, Marjorie. "Water Buoyancy, Cohesion & Adhesion." Kids Discover. Accessed August 20, 2016. http://www.kidsdiscover.com/teacherresources/water-buoyancy-cohesion-adhesion/.

"Goldburger to Go!" Zoom. PBS Kids. Accessed August 10, 2016. http://pbskids.org/zoom/games/goldburgertogo/realworld.html.

"Gravity: Facts." Science Trek. Idaho Public Television. Accessed August 5, 2016. http://idahoptv.org/sciencetrek/topics/gravity/facts.cfm.

"How to Make a SIMPLE Rube Goldberg Machine—Become a Beginner." YouTube. Accessed August 23, 2016. https://youtu.be/PK2_gA2OeMI.

Krulwich, Robert. "What Is It About Bees and Hexagons?" Krulwich Wonders. NPR. Accessed August 12, 2016. http://www.npr.org/sections/krulwich/2013/05/13/183704091/what-is-it-about-bees-and-hexagons.

"Lesson Plan: Creating a Student Produced Weather Forecast." School Video News. Accessed July 27, 2016. http://schoolvideonews.com/Lesson-Plans-Curriculum/Lesson-Plan-Creating-a-Student-Produced-Weather-Forecast.

"The Magnet Maze." Museum of Science, Boston. Accessed July 16, 2016. http://www.mos.org/sites/dev-elvis.mos.org/files/docs/education/mos_observing-electricity-magnets_magnet-maze.pdf.

"Mobility Solutions for Dogs." Handicapped Pets Inc. Accessed August 19, 2016. http://www.handicappedpets.com/mobility-solutions-for-dogs.

National Oceanic and Atmospheric Adminsitration. Accessed August 27, 2016. http://www.noaa.gov/.

Notes from a Small Apiary (blog). Accessed August 12, 2016. http://apiarynotes.blogspot.com/.

Oblack, Rachelle. How to Use Weather Maps to Make a Forecast. Accessed August 10, 2016. http://weather.about.com/od/lessonplanshighschool/a/How-To-Use-Weather-Maps-To-Make-A-Forecast.htm.

"Rube Goldberg Contraptions." Teaching Channel. Accessed August 10, 2016. https://www.teachingchannel.org/videos/rube-goldberg-contraptions.

"Rube Goldberg Machine Contests." Rube Goldberg Inc. Accessed August 10, 2016. https://www.rubegoldberg.com/education/contest/.

Silverman, Jacob. "Why Do Beavers Build Dams?" How Stuff Works: Animals. Accessed July 21, 2016. http://animals.howstuffworks.com/mammals/beaver-dam1.htm.

"Solar Basics." Energy Kids. U.S. Energy Information Administration. Accessed August 19, 2016. http://www.eia.gov/KIDS/energy.cfm?page=solar_home-basics.

"Teaching Beyond the Textbook with Magnets." PBS Learning Media California. Accessed July 16, 2016. http://www.pbslearningmedia.org/resource/tdpd12.pd.sci.magbeyond/teaching-beyond-the-textbook-with-magnets/.

"Weather." About.com. Accessed August 10, 2016. http://weather.about.com/.

"Weather and Climate." NASA's Climate Kids. Accessed August 18, 2016. http://climatekids.nasa.gov/menu/weather-and-climate/.

"Weather Safety." Weather Wiz Kids. Accessed July 21, 2016. http://www.weatherwizkids.com/weather-safety.htm.

"The WeatherSTEM Alert Platform." WeatherSTEM. Accessed August 27, 2016. www.weatherstem.com.

"What Do You Call a Honey Bees House?" Hive and Honey Apiary. Accessed August 12, 2016. http://www.hiveandhoneyapiary com/Honeybeeshouse.html.

"What Is a Fossil?" The Learning Zone. Oxford University Museum of Natural History. Accessed August 2, 2016. http://www.oum.ox.ac.uk/thezone/fossils/intro/index.htm.

"What Makes Bridges So Strong?" SciShow Kids. Accessed June 24, 2016. https://www.youtube.com/watch?v=oVOnRPefcno.

"What Makes Paper Airplanes Fly?" Teachers. Scholastic Inc. Accessed June 23, 2016. http://www.scholastic.com/teachers/article/what-makes-paper-airplanes-fly.